Helsingør Station
& Other Departures

AIDAN HIGGINS

Helsingør Station & Other Departures

Fictions & Autobiographies 1956–1989

SECKER & WARBURG
London

First published in Great Britain 1989
by Martin Secker & Warburg Limited,
Michelin House, 81 Fulham Road,
London SW3 6RB

A CIP catalogue record for this book
is available from the British Library

ISBN 0 436 19550 X

'Killachter Meadow' and 'Lebensraum' were first published in Felo de Se (John
Calder, 1960; reissued in 1978 as Asylum and Other Stories); 'Frère Jacques, Bruder
Jacques' first appeared in Firebird 4 (Penguin Books, 1985); 'Helsingør Station' in
London Magazine, 1974; 'The Other Day I Was Thinking of You' in Ambit, 1986;
'Beneath the Ice-shelf' in London Review of Books, 1974; 'Anthony Burgess at the
London Savoy' in the Sunday Tribune, 1980.

An early draft of 'Sodden Fields' (entitled 'Imaginary Meadows') appeared in
Fiction Magazine, 1985, and a preliminary version of 'The Bird I Fancied' was
published in Modern Irish Stories (Irish Times, 1985).

Photoset by Deltatype, Ellesmere Port, South Wirral
Printed and Bound in Great Britain
by Richard Clay Ltd, Bungay, Suffolk

Contents

For Alannah, *¡adelante!*

The ghosts die as we grow older, they die and their places are taken by real ghosts . . . The happiest days become the saddest afterwards; let us never go back, lest we too die.

Richard Jefferies (1848–87)

Killachter Meadow

1956

The remains of Miss Emily Norton Kervick were committed to the grave one cold day in March of 1927. On that morning – the third – a Mass for the Dead had been offered for the repose of her soul, and she was buried without delay in Griffenwrath cemetery.

The day previously the body had been laid out on its high bed in a room too full of the stupefying odour of arum lilies. It had been her bedroom. The furnishings were not remarkable. A fierce wallpaper design of bamboo and prodigal shoots appeared to contract the walls on two sides. Within that area and resting on the bare boards, white and sedate, decked with flowers, stood the death-bed. This bed, notwithstanding its panoply, notwithstanding its character of unmistakable intent, or its occupant, seemed to move on its castors at a slow, almost imperceptible rate of its own – as small craft in a difficult roadstead will creep from their moorings.

Then the room shook under the tread of mourners. They came unsolicited on the first day, a mixed bag of male and female gentry come to pay what they described as 'their last respects'. Wearing the appropriate expression they took up a position by the bed-head. They were not relatives but locals. And every so often they so far forgot themselves as to make that hurried, somewhat cupid-inous gesture of piety – blessed themselves. Emily-May's forbidding manner had repulsed them in life and now, destitute of sense, it finally routed them.

This corpse, so exact and still, was impervious to all human compassion; their presence seemed superfluous or worse – as though uninvited they had arrived at the wrong funeral. In the hotpress her linen lay stored and ready; her cases stood packed in the next room. It did not seem that she had died and escaped them; on the contrary, dead, she had come to stay.

She offered no help herself, being content to lie there, grey and heavy, dressed in a monk's dark habit which even covered her upturned toes, clutching rosary beads cumbersome as manacles. The head was thrust back into the folds of the cowl, out of which an arrogant warrior's nose and pronounced cheekbones appeared in a scarred and discoloured face. On her chest, in addition, was balanced a phenomenally heavy crucifix. In posture she resembled a Crusader in a tomb, seemingly just on the point of rising up violently and dashing the Cross to the ground: the general effect being more military than strictly religious.

Warily the survivors circled this ambiguous death-bed, half conscious of the permutations it had already undergone, hoping it had gone through them all. Now boat-like on no high seas; now solid and as though cast in rock like a tomb; now shrunken to the dimensions of a litter. So they could make nothing of it and had to retire baffled. A day later the bed itself lay stripped and empty. Death had borne the last disquieting image of Emily Norton Kervick down with it into the grave.

I

Forty-five years before, in the hopeful 1880s, a couple by the name of Kervick bought Springfield House outright from the Land Commission for the purpose of farming and raising a family. Springfield House was a freehold premises in the barony of old Killachter, situated one mile from Celbridge village and the ramparts of Marley Abbey, whilom home of Hester Vanhomrigh.

Two decades later this couple had passed away, unmourned and almost forgotten in their own time, leaving

behind as a legacy for four unprepossessing and unmar-
riageable daughters a seventy-two acre estate so fallen into
neglect that it had to be parcelled out as grazing land. Over
the years the rockery and vegetable gardens had merged to
become a common wilderness. In the orchard the untrimmed branches sank until lost in the dense uprising of grass.
Four spinsters grew up there. They were christened, in order
of appearance: Emily Norton (known as Emily-May), Tess,
Helen, Imogen.

Imogen Kervick had the nondescript face of a plaster
madonna, pallor and all. Her small opportunist mouth
daubed with dark lipstick was modelled on Louise Brooks
and she favoured also the trench-coats and the hats of the
time. Her movements were at once prosaic and portentous;
she conjured up lascivious dreamy knees for herself, and a
heart full of vicissitudes, the morals of a rhesus monkey.
From her a declaration of love would have to be as detailed
as a death-sentence; fortunately the occasion never arose.
Imprisoned in her own particular folly, she refused to
behave as if there were any such condition as *âge dangereux*
or any such policy as relenting. She preferred to represent
herself as if lodged within a ring of persecution – making
considered motions with the hand, waiting only for the
faggots to be lit under her. Sometimes, laying down her
knife and fork, she wept at table, her eyes wide open and no
tears falling.

It was into this unlikely subject that Cupid had discharged
his bolts. Some years previously she had created a modest
stir by indulging her fancy with a pallid youth named
Klaefisch. No one had ever looked at him before, least of all a
woman, least of all with favour. He came from Bavaria. He
had one good lung, and resembled a gawky version of
Constantine Guys. It was she who persuaded him to live
with them, but outside, like a dog, in a clapboard and tar
edifice that stood on raised ground. Here Otto Klaefisch
came for peace and quiet, for free board or a little love – if
that was to be part of the price; but mainly in order to
complete his three-year-old thesis, *Das Soziale Schicksal in den
Novellen Theodor Storms*.

Throughout that summer the swallows went shrieking overhead, and Imogen came and went from the house with tray after tray of food. She walked boldly into the pavilion and came out later carrying pages for typing scored with a bold Gothic script. Did he make attempts on her virtue in there? Nobody knew. From the frameless window the face of the nine days' wonder peered, the sun glinting on bifocals and the corners of his mouth drawn down.

Gliding past of an evening they heard his nasal drone punctuating the dark. It was Otto reciting Schiller to himself. (*'Der Mensch muss hinaus ins feindliche Leben,'* muttered Otto darkly, *'muss wirken und streben!'*) Indifferent to them, he was travelled, well read, uncommunicative, loose-living, free. But this idyll of late-flowering love was of short duration.

For one short summer only Otto tolerated her ardours. For one season only were they treated to the unedifying spectacle of a spinster-virgin in rut, their shameless sister. Then one day she found herself alone again with the three resident she-devils. Otto had departed with his thesis, finished and bound in dark blue leather.

The weeks and the years passed almost unnoticed. The weeds grew upwards, rotted, passed away. The wheel of the seasons spun round; quite soon she had forgotten him. Like her sisters she was lost in a career of unblemished idleness. She had some sort of an understanding with Helen. Sometimes they talked to each other for hours at a stretch. When she and Helen came to speak together, each had to rise to the surface in order to say what they had to say, after which they sank again to their respective depths.

Tess was the eldest but one. Of her let it be said, she played Demon Patience for her nerves, liked to work in the garden for her health, drank gin for preference, enjoyed outside contacts, was Joseph's employer. She had red hair, buck teeth and a child's high voice. Tess was a Patroness of Adversity, and a pawn to the others' kings and queens. She is not in this story.

The third daughter was Helen.

Helen Kervick was a collector of dead things, right from the start. She discarded dolls (capable of modestly lowering their eyes) in favour of rabbits strangled in the snares and overrun with lice and fleas, and these she disentangled and buried with her own hands. It was they, dumb disfigured creatures, who got all her compassion, as she grew up. She went her own way, inventing games for herself alone that required no partners. All her life that tendency would continue – the game that required neither the presence nor the assistance of a second party.

'I just live for the day,' she said, 'and I try not to think of anything much . . .'

She sat often in the window-seat in the sun, sometimes manufacturing dark rings under her eyes with a typewriter brush.

II

Emily-May was the fourth, the first-born, the heaviest by far. In her distant youth she had been a holy terror on the tennis court, performing in a headband and one of Papa's discarded cricket shirts, worn moody and loose, panting about the court, perspiring under her armpits. Languidly she moved to serve. Heavily she served, elaborate and inaccurate, recalling to mind the high action of obsolete field-pieces. She toed the base-line, measured Tess's ground with a merciless eye, served. Into the net went the ball. Again. She threw the service ball high into the air, squared at it, refused the strike, re-caught it! At a third or even fourth attempt she might be induced, with much caracoling, to make a stroke – the sun flashing on the racquet and the ball once again crashing into the net.

All through summer endless games of singles were contested with the patient Tess. Rallies were infrequent. Some of the high returns had to be retrieved from the beech hedge with a long stepladder. Tess kept the score.

'Thirty-fiff!' she cried in her intolerable tennis voice. *'Thirty-fiff!'*

Missel-thrushes came floating down from the great trees

into the evergreens. Dusk crept around Springfield. The sun descended into the wood. Tess served again. Emily-May, model of rectitude, crouched in the Helen Wills Moody position. Dim figures stirred again. It had all happened in the long ago.

Otherwise Emily-May's gestures betrayed few emotions. Her gestures and progress, reduced to a minimum, were as uniformly dull as her clothes. Her face, a full pod of flesh, was bulky and uneasy; her manner was so abashed that it could only be seen or thought of by degrees. For there are such faces. Her entire corporal presence had the unknown quality of things stared at so often that they are no longer seen. Her condition was one of constant and virtually unrelieved embarrassment. Here was a person who had run out of enthusiasms early on in life, and in the halls of her spirit, so to speak, toadstools grew. Imogen, who detested her, had appointed herself Emily-May's biographer and amanuensis. But all the thin slanders assembled by her bounced harmlessly off the sebaceous elder, whom few cared to address directly. Emily-May took ridiculously small steps for a person of her bulk and moved rapidly, pigeon-toed, from thick-set hips with a repressed fury that was painful to see. Physically she belonged to what Kretschmer called the pyknic type (all arse and occiput). Add to this a disagreeable set of countenance and an uncommon air, for a lady, of suffering from hypertrophy of the prostate. The creature had commenced to put on flesh at an early age, and as well as that found herself prematurely bald before the age of thirty. Those unhappy people who speak of being 'thrown back' upon themselves, in the sense of being confounded, would perhaps have understood her best. For she was a throwback, stem and corolla risen to new heights, bound to please no one; one single forbidding link, alive and growing into itself, casting a brave shadow in a world loathsome beyond words, from root to flower.

Poultry abounded in the back yard, a hundred yards away from the house. Everything from fidgety bantams to turkeys, spurred and fierce, savagely disposed towards all, were allowed their freedom there.

Helen was greatly attached to the hens and their little ways and liked nothing better than to spend hours observing them. This she did with the aid of a collapsible camp-stool, moving about from point to point in their wake, and then sitting stock-still in her battered old hat, not knowing her mind between one beat of her heart and the next. Endlessly patient she sat there, Crusoe with his beginnings. The hens themselves seemed to live in a lifelong coma, disturbed only by the rats who sought to catch them on the ground at night; or by Joseph, ready to lay violent hands on them by day – for though Helen herself was a vegetarian both Tess and Emily-May were gluttons for spring chicken served with new potatoes.

While they lived the hens collected grubs, flies, took dust-baths, waited for the cock to rush upon them and have his way; sometimes they ventured far afield into the meadows. The evening was their time. They seemed happier then, a little surer of themselves. They sang in a cracked unhinged key that rose, more lament than song, hesitated (they were sure of nothing), broke off before the phrase ended. Up the ramp at dusk they stumbled after the white cock, and one by one they dropped inside.

They were early astir in the morning in the dock-and-pollen-infested yard, scratching and rooting about, emitting sad droning cries, *Key-key-kee-kee-keeeeee*, that then trickled off into silence. One of their number would sometimes take fright, call out three or four times, then stand petrified as all the other red hens froze about the yard. A dog was moving behind the wall; a hawk was hovering above, preparing to fall out of the sky and rend one of them. Then that danger too seemed to pass. The first one would move again, dipping its head and clucking. Then one by one all would resume their activities as before. They seemed pleased with the filthiest surroundings – the lime-fouled henhouse or the big troughs. Imogen it was who fed them. They got into the mush the better to enjoy it.

Helen spent whole days among them, listening to their talk; in it there was neither statement, question, nor reply; and this characteristic greatly pleased her.

*

Helen sat indoors, uncomfortably on her raised seat in the upper cabin, lost in *The Anatomy of Melancholy*. The last daylight swam in the clouded pockets of the little window, as from a bathysphere, before her eyes. Evening clouds were moving across that portion of the sky visible to her. She was thinking of Emily-May, about whom she was attempting to write something (closing her Burton and shutting her eyes). Her eldest sister, who from the tenderest age onwards could be seen lurking in the background in a succession of family snapshots, invariably surprised in a slovenly pose, off-guard, her weight resting on one hip – effacing herself, so that she became more distant than a distant relative. But she did this so well it had become almost indelicate to notice it. Well, she had been foundering in some such confusion all her life – a life lonely and shy, subjected to a process of erosion that had reduced her in some irreparable way. Until at last she came to resemble that other person trapped in the snapshot, a version of herself perpetuated in some anxious pose and unable to walk forward out of that paralysis.

The cabin was flooded with a white afterlight, an emulsion reflected from a non-existent sea. The sun was setting. Evening Benediction had begun. Helen stared through the glass and never saw the dogs moving cautiously about the yard, for her mind's eye was fixed on other things.

In the hot summers and sometimes even in winter, Emily-May went bathing more or less every day, naked into the river. Grotesque in modesty as in everything else, she crept down to the water, both chubby hands shielding her various allurements, overpowering as the goddess Frigga at the bath. Avoiding the main current (for she could not swim) she floated awkwardly downriver in the shallows, using one fat leg as a keel, touching bottom, floating on. At such times she was happy, no longer caring that she might be seen and find herself in the Court of Assizes on a charge of indecent exposure, and she no longer feared that she might drown. The noises of the river delighted her, the sensation of floating also, the nakedness too. Her nerves relented, she let go, she was calm, she felt free.

Thus did Emily-May indulge herself all day long in the summer. After these excursions she had the whetted appetite of a female Cyclops. Shoulders of beef, haunches of lamb, fish and poultry and game, washed down with soup and beer, all these and many more condiments disappeared into that voracious crop. She lived in indescribable squalor among the scattered remains of Scotch shortbread, preserves, chewed ends of anchovy toast, boxes of *glacé* fruit, rounds of digestive biscuits lurid with greengage jam. Indoors and out she ate, day and night, winter and summer, odds and ends in the pantry, lettuce and bananas with cold rabbit by the river. But little of what her mouth contained was by her ferocious stomach received, no, but from rapidly champing jaws did fall and by the passing current was carried away, *secundum carnem*.

In her lair, safe from intrusion, Helen wrote into her day-book: 'As a person may mime from a distance "I-have-been-unavoidably-delayed", by a subtle displacement of dignity, such as the wry face, the hapless gesture of the hand etc, etc, so Emily-May's manner of walking has become the equivalent of the shrug of the shoulders. The fear of becoming the extreme sort of person she might, in other circumstances, have become has thrown her far back. The pattern of a final retreat runs through her like a grain in rough delft.'

None of this high-flown Della Cruscan pleasing her, Helen broke off, closing her book and putting aside her pencil. She looked out. The yard gates stood wide apart. Great dogs were lifting their hind legs and wetting the doors of outhouses – acts mannered and ceremonial as in a Votive Mass. Peace reigned in Griffenwrath. Then far away in the fields some-one called. Helen threw open the window. Amazed, the dogs took to their heels. Helen drew in her head and went quietly downstairs.

III

Joseph the gardener sat drinking stout under a prunus tree

out of the heat of day. The shambles of his awkward feet lay before him, side by side and abject in their thick woollen socks. He had removed his boots and laid them aside. A smell of captive sweat pervaded his person and something else too, the stench of something in an advanced state of decay.

Joseph killed silently and with the minimum of effort. His victims the hens had scarcely time to cry out, before they were disembowelled. Fowl and vermin were dispatched with equal impartiality, for he was their slaughterman. He was a great punter too. His speculating on the turf met with an almost unqualified lack of success, but this did not deter him in the least. His drab waistcoat blazed with insignia – half were seed catalogues and half rejected betting slips.

A passive and indolent man by nature, he spent his working day among the moss-roses and privets, or kneeling among the azaleas – weeding, praying, farting, no one knew. He spent much time in such poses, and it required quite a feat of imagination to see him upright and on the move. Yet move he did – a crab but recently trodden on who must struggle back to find first its legs, torn off by an aggressor, and then its element. His balance was only restored to him when in position, in servitude, behind a wheelbarrow, say, or a rake. He knew his place, and kept himself to himself.

Labouring in the garden, on which his labours made so little impression, he kept his Wild Woodbines out of harm's way under his hat, with the lunch. He was their gardener, he was indispensable, he knew it. Joseph the mock-father lay sleeping under the prunus tree, pandering to a chronic ataraxy.

He was the person who saw most of Helen, all that there was to be seen of Helen. She spent most of her time indoors, drawn up like a bat in daylight behind the window curtains on the first floor. Groping in the earth sometimes he felt her eyes fixed upon him. Turning to see, framed in the darkness of the window where the progress of the creeper was broken, the white face of the recluse staring at him. Half-risen he then attempted a salute (as if taking aim with a gun) from which she turned away. The gesture could not be repeated. She was reading.

The other three women seldom saw her, lacking either the energy or the interest to raise their tired eyes. They passed to and fro below, plucking at themselves and mumbling, exercising soberly about the various levels of the garden, fond of the tangled grottos, trailing through shade like insane persons or nuns of a silent order.

A great impressive hedge, a beech, eighteen feet high, ran the length of the garden; beyond it lay the orchard. Alongside this hedge Emily-May had worn a path hard and smooth in her regular patrols, tramping down the pretty things, a veritable Juggernaut, the colt's-foot, the valerian, the dock. It bore her onward, at night shining under her like a stream. Her shadow moved below like a ship's hull.

At long intervals Helen too appeared in the garden. After winter rain she liked to walk in the orchard. Joseph spied on her, marvelling as the grey engaged figure urged itself on among the stunted trees, appearing and disappearing again, like something recorded.

At other times she left the window open and gramophone music started above his head. She sang foreign songs in a melancholy drawn-out fashion, more chant than song, and not pleasant either way. She sang:

> *Es brennt mir unter beiden Sohlen,*
> *Tret' ich auch schon auf Eis und SCHNEEEE!*

Joseph covered his ears; this was too much. Night once more was falling on this graceless Mary, on her fondest aspirations as on her darkest fears – the confusion of one day terminating in the confusion of the next. Joseph, in his simplicity, believed that she had been something in vaudeville, in another country.

Urge, urge, urge; dogs gnawing.

IV

The apartment was cluttered with an assortment of casual tables on which stood divers bottles and jars. A submarine light filtered through the angled slots of the Venetian blinds, dust swirling upwards in its wake, passing slowly through sunlight and on up out of sight. A frieze could be distinguished, depicting a seaside scene, presented as a flat statement in colour as though for children (the room had formerly been a nursery), beneath which at calculated intervals hung a line of heavily built ancestors in gilt frames, forbidding in aspect as a rogues' gallery, leaning into the room as from the boxes of a theatre.

Out of the depths of a tattered armchair Helen's pale features began to emerge, as Imogen went towards her, to the sound of defunct springs. A miscellaneous collection of fur and feathered life moved as she moved, flitting into obscure hiding-places. High above their strong but unnameable smell rose the fetid reek of old newspapers. In one corner a great pile had mounted until jammed between floor and ceiling, like clenched teeth. An unknown number of chiming clocks kept up a morose-sounding chorus, announcing the hours with subdued imprecision. Even in high summer the place gave off a succession of offensive cold-surface smells: an unforgettable blend of rotting newspaper, iodine, mackintosh, cat.

Here on this day and at this hour was Helen Jeanne Kervick, spinster and potential authoress, at home and receiving. In the gloom her voice came faint as from another person in a distant room – a weak and obstinate old voice:

'And our dead ones,' she was saying, 'our parents, do you think of them? When we were young they were old already. And when we in turn were no longer young, why they seemed hardly to have changed. They went past us in the end, crackling like parchment.'

She stirred in her antique chair. After a while she went on:

'Do you suppose they intercede for us now, in Heaven, before the throne of Almighty God? Now that they have become what they themselves always spoke so feelingly of – "the Dear Departed" – when they were alive? Oh my God,' she said with feeling, 'what will become of us all, and how will it all end?'

Imogen said nothing, watching Helen's long unringed

14

fingers stroking the upholstery of her chair. The friction produced a fine dust that rose like smoke. Beyond it, in it, Helen's voice continued:

'Ah, how can we be expected to behave in a manner that befits a lady? – how can we? Everything is moving' (a motion of the hand) 'and I don't move quickly enough. Yes, yes, we envy the thing we cannot be. So, we're alive, yes, that's certain. It's certain that we're old women. At least we stink as old women should.'

It was the beginning of a long rambling tirade.

Like all Helen's tirades, it had the inconclusive character of a preamble. As she spoke, pausing for a word here, losing track of the argument there, the captive wildlife began to grow increasingly restive.

'We take everything into account, everything except the baseness of God's little images. What a monster he must be! We've set ourselves up here like scarecrows and only frighten the life out of one another when we come up against ourselves in the wrong light. And in winter the damned sky comes down until it's hanging over our ears, and all we can think about are the mundane things of the world and its rottenness. And then there's that bald glutton Emily-May having seizures in her bottomless pit, and we can't even distinguish her screams from the noises in our heads.'

She stopped, and sat silent for a long time. Then she said:

'When one lives in the country long enough, one begins to see the cities as old and queer. It's like looking back centuries.'

She went on:

'Listen, have you ever considered this: that Crusoe's life could only cease to be intolerable when he stopped looking for a sail and resigned himself to living with his dependants under a mountain – have you ever thought of that? No. Trust in providence, my dear, and remember, no roc is going to sit on its eggs until they are hatched out of all proportions; or if there ever was such a bird, I haven't heard of her.'

From by the door Imogen's voice called something. Drawing closer then and pointing a finger, she said in a child's high voice:

'Dust hath closed Helen's eyes.'

Something hard struck Helen's forehead and she allowed herself to fall back without another word. She heard feet lagging on the stairs and after that silence again. Pressing fingers to her brow like electrodes she bent forward until she was almost stifling. A heady smell of dust, undisturbed by time, and the parochial odour of her own person entered her throat and filled her eyes with unshed tears. Something began to ring, blow upon blow, in her head. She straightened up again with a hand to her heart and listened.

A distant sound of wild ringing in the air.

It was the workmen's bell in Killadoon that was tolling. Faint and drifting, carried hither, finally ceasing. Almost, for there was the aftertone. There it was again, the last of it. She felt relieved. The men had finished another day of labour and were departing on their bicycles. From the shelter of the trees she had watched them go. That heavy and toilsome lift of the leg, and then away, slowly home under the walnut trees, past the lodge-gate, down the long back drive of Colonel Clement's estate, home to their sausages and tea.

Blood was groping and fumbling in her, pounding through her, greedy lungs and mean heart. 'Bleed no more, Helen Kervick, bleed no more!' the blood said. No more the thin girl-child, no more the anaemic spinster; no more of it. She rose and dusted her person. Where now?

She crossed to the window and peered through the blinds at what remained of the day. High-scudding cloud, the wood, sky on the move, feeling of desolation. Already she regretted everything she had said to Imogen. Yes, every word. It was all vanity and foolishness. And herself just a bit of time pushed to the side. That was all. She heaved a sigh, allowed the slat to fall back into place and stepped back.

The door stood open. Dusk was everywhere in the room. The landing lay below her, bathed in a spectral light. She stepped down onto its faded surface. Her mind was still disturbed; she was thinking of the departing men. They dug in the earth; they knew it, through and through; it was their element; things grew for them. One day they too would be

16

put down into it themselves, parting the sods and clay easily, going down like expert divers.

'The faith,' they said, 'have you not the faith?' She had not. It was something they carried about with them, not to be balked, heavy and reliable, like themselves. She felt at peace in their company. They were solid men; but their faith was repugnant to her. Their stiff genuflecting, as if on sufferance, and their labourers' hands locked in prayer (for she had gone to Mass to be among them) – their contrite hearts. Out of all this, which in her heart she detested, she was locked. And yet they offered her peace. How did that come about?

Here Tess, tired of waiting for the evening cock-pheasant to put in an appearance, strolled out from behind a tree in the field below and began to move along the plantation edge, as though she had intended something else.

V

Members of the Kervick family, too old now to have any sense, strolled vaguely about the house and along the landings, appearing suddenly in rooms sealed off since the death of their parents. Sometimes their heads showed in the currant bushes; at other periods they stood under the plum tree with their mouths half open. They began to collect loganberries industriously in a bowl by the loganberry wall. They cut wasps out of the last apples and worms out of the last pears in the fall. There was a time when Helen could scarcely walk into the garden without flushing out one of them – such was their patience – collapsed onto a rustic seat and lost in some wretched reverie or dolour. For the combined misery of the Kervick *Lebensgefühl* was oppressive enough to turn the Garden of Eden into another Gethsemane overnight.

Plucking up courage, they would set off for unknown destinations on high antiquated bicycles, pedalling solemnly down the wrong drives and out of sight for the day. Dressed in her Louis XV green, Tess was bound for the back road and

Lady Ismay's gin. Emily-May herself was off again to paint in Castletown demesne. In the course of a long career over four hundred versions of the houses and reaches of the river, drawn from the life, had been accumulated, most of them duplicates.

At a bend in the front drive, where the paling interfered with Helen's line of sight, watching from the window, the cyclist (it was Emily-May, gross and splendid with a hamper strapped onto the rear carrier) jerked forward out of perspective as if sliced in two – the upper section travelling on, astonished and alone, with augmented rapidity. It was not unknown for one or both of the cyclists to return in a suspicious condition; but unsober or not they never returned together.

Alone and safe from intrusion now, Helen crouched in her sky cabin. Alternating between it and the window-seat, she relied on her mood and on the waning light to inform her where to go. Indeed at any time of the day or night the curtains might part and Helen Kervick palely emerge, clad from head to toe in *bouclé* tweed, clutching her Burton or translations from the Latin masters, making her way to the bright convenience on the upper landing. Her head was sometimes seen suspended from that window with hair swinging in her eyes. After dark she closed the curtains carefully behind her, extinguished the oil lamp, passed down the main stairs to the hall, ignoring the dim print of Lady Elizabeth Butler's *Scotland for Ever!*, arriving on the gravel dressed for walking. In the window-seat in winter she bore patiently the cold and the affront of continuous rain, sighing down her life for the last time again – on the garden, on labouring Joseph, on the parallels, on the flying rain. Stay Time a while thy flying.

Air!

VI

Towards midday, the weather being fine and bright, early March weather, Joseph appeared with a tremendous rake and began to scuffle the gravel before the house, but without much heart and not for long. Somewhere a window went up and a sharp voice called his name.

He did not appear to hear: an image dark and labouring in the weak sun with a halo of light above his head, outside the world of tears and recrimination, his gloom cast for all time. But there was no escaping.

'TEA!' the voice screamed.

Joseph came to a halt and removed his hat.

'Oh come along now, Joseph!' the high bright voice invited mellifluously.

.

Emily-May freewheeled by Paisley's corner for the last time and soon had passed Marley Abbey on her right hand. Vanessa's old home. Swift had gone there on horseback, jig, jig, long ago. Emily-May went coasting on into the village. She ordered half a dozen Guinness from Dan Breen and began, on account of the gradient, to walk her bicycle uphill towards the great demesne gates. She passed the convent where with the other little girls of First Infants she had studied her Catechism. Later, in First Communion veils, models of rectitude, they sang in childish trebles, '*O salutaris hostia*' and '*Tantum ergo*'. Bowing her head she passed in silence through Castletown gates – the skeleton branches rigid above her, Emily-May descended into her nether world.

Core, Hart, Hole, Keegan, Kervick, Coyle. Damp forgotten life; passing, passing. Some had lived at Temple Mill, some at Great Tarpots, and some at Shatover. Molly North lived at St Helen's Court: she had long black hair and was beautiful, unlike Emily-May who had tow hair and was considered hideous.

She passed through. Beyond March's bare trees she saw the sun hammering on the river: the water flowed by like a muscle, the summer returned, something turned over in Emily-May and she became young and voluptuous once more (she had never been either). A few minutes later she had reached her secret place behind a clump of pampas grass. She spared herself nothing. Trembling she began to undo her buttons and release her powerful elastic girdle. She, a stout Christian who could not swim a stroke to save her life, pulled off her remaining drawers, charged into the piercing water and struck out at a dog-crawl. The damp morning

19

was like so much sugar in her blood. The bitterly cold water ate into her spine as the main current began to draw her downstream. Under wet hanging branches she was carried, dropping her keel, touching nothing but water. By fields, by grazing cattle, by calm estate walls, Emily Odysseus Kervick drifted, the last of her line, without issue, distinction or hope. She could not cry out; frozen to the bone now, steered by no passing bell, she floated weirwards towards extinction and forgetting. The river carried her on, the clay banks rearing up on either side, and there she seemed to see her little sisters, grown minute as dolls, playing their old games. She saw Tess clearly and behind, holding her hand, the infant Imogen. She screamed once, but they neither heard nor answered and after a while they ran away. Suddenly, directly overhead, Helen's crafty face appeared. She looked straight down, holding in her hands the fishing lines. As a child Emily-May had a passion for writing her name and address on sheets of paper, plugging them into bottles and dropping them in the river below the mill. She imagined now that Helen had remembered this too, and that Helen alone could retrieve or save her. But when she looked again Helen had become a child. Innocence had bestowed on her sister another nature, an ideal nature outside corruption and change, watched over by herslf – drowned, grown more ugly and more remote – so that the decades and decades of her own life, past now, seemed a series of mechanical devices arranged at intervals like the joints of a telescope held inverted to the eye – to distort everything she inspected and to separate her from life and from whatever happiness life had to offer. Brought sharply into focus, it became clear that Helen had not escaped to a later innocence, not at all, but in growing up had merely adopted a series of disguises, each one more elaborate and more perfect, leaving her essential nature unchanged. As they stared hopelessly into each other's faces something altered in Helen's. For an instant the child's face was overlaid by the adult face known to Emily-May – this one a mask, long and perverted. It stared down unmoved on her wretchedness – naked, 'presumed lost' – itself empty of expression, disfigured now, as though beyond participation. (Here Helen herself closed her Burton and rose up sighing. As her foot touched the floor she drew down the chain with a nervous disengaged hand.)

But the dark gulf was already opening for her sister. Swept

towards it by an unbearable wind, courage and endurance (she never had either) ceased to matter. Emily-May saw that and closed her eyes on the roaring, the ROARING. The rockery and roaring gardens were together under the weeds, the untrimmed branches in the orchard were lost; lost until all, prostrate and rank, sank from human sight.

Lebensraum

1957

I

Fräulein Sevi Klein left Germany in the spring of her thirty-ninth year; travelling alone from Cologne to Ostend, she crossed the Channel, and from Folkestone to London found herself in the company of sober British citizens. She took a reserved seat facing the engine on the London train, her feet on the carriage floor as settled as ball-and-claw furniture, both fierce-looking and 'arranged' after the manner of such extremities, curving downwards towards a relentless grip. Her hips and spine conveyed the same impression, but reinforced, becoming the downturned head of a dumb creature with muzzle lowered as though drinking; her eyelids seemed an intolerable weight. Her knees were pressed modestly together, she had hands of remarkable beauty and dressed in a manner suitable for someone possibly ten years younger. At Victoria Station she hired a cab, read out the name of a Kensington hotel from her pocket-book and was driven there with a moderate amount of luggage strapped into the boot. This was in the summer of 1947.

Sevi Klein walked the streets with the rolling gait of a sailor. In the National Gallery she stood minute below the paintings of Veronese, marvelling at his immense hot-faced women. Here she had met her match, for she was a lady herself down to the cockpit, but below that a snake chitterling or a chitterling snake.

Inevitably she walked into trouble at night on the Bayswater Road. The whores told her exactly what she could do with herself in Cockney and French, a dark one pouring baleful abuse into one ear, brandishing a copy of the Sierra Leone *Observer*. She said:

'*Vergiss es*,' thinking she preferred the Brinkgasse. Several times she was accosted by late gentlemen passing in Palace Avenue, until she took to scaling the fence into Kensington Gardens. She sat on the cement edge of the Round Pond with both feet submerged, the red glow of her cigarette reflected in the water between her legs; leaning forward until the monotonous passage of ingoing and outgoing traffic on Bayswater Road became dulled and remote. After a while she heard only the wind in the trees and the stirrings of the geese across from her. At last she threw away her cigarette and sat with the edge of her skirt trailing in the water, hearing nothing.

Her flat was a dark place into which an uncertain sun never entered, but in summer loitered for a couple of hours on the balcony before creeping away. She opened the full-length windows to sit drinking coffee in the sun, dropping her ash through the iron grid, staring into the chestnut tree opposite. On odd Sundays the terrace resounded to the deafening strains of an itinerant drum-and-accordion band.

The whores continued to be suspicious of her. A freelance who lived in the basement next door had noticed her nocturnal habits and irregular hours of business and passed on the information. She roamed the streets with an air free yet constrained, like a castaway. Growing attached to Kensington Gardens she liked to spend whole days there in summer dressed as briefly as decency would permit, sitting on a deckchair under the hawthorns. She read constantly and brought out a covered basket of sandwiches and cold beer. She enjoyed drinking but missed the bitter Kölsch beer of *Vater Rhein*.

In dull weather the gardens were deserted at evening save for old women exercising dogs. Then she went sauntering down the avenues of trees beyond the equestrian statue, heading for the Serpentine, a small figure silhouetted for an instant where the lanes ran together, dwindling, shapeless, then blotted out. Her favourite pub was by the Queensway Underground. An already strong thirst was improved every time she passed the entrance and caught the dead air carried up by the lift. Then the gates crashed to on another lift full of pale commuters – the light vanishing as the contraption sank from sight.

One evening in June of that year she had drunk a little too much again and was flushed and talkative; meeting her reflection in one of the mirrors behind the bar, she knew it. The mirrors created an hexagonal smoke-filled confusion, and in these the patrons would sometimes encounter unexpectedly their own befuddled stares directed back at them from unlikely angles between shining tunnels of bottles. There upon the reflection of her own features another's strange features sank. A question was directed at her. Looking up she came face to face with a Mr Michael Alpin, late of Dublin, the doubtful product of Jesuit casuistry and the Law School. As far as the eye could see the patrons, with downcast eyes, were drinking their anxious beer. On one side a drunk repeated:

'Fizzillogical . . .' (inaudible) – 'Swizzer-land . . . Yes, shir,' and a sober one said over and over again: 'Really I don't know whether to buy that house or not . . . now really I don't.' An elderly gentleman who had blown his nose too hard had to leave his drink and retire bleeding to the toilets. But Michael Alpin looked down into the small crucified face under the love-locks with the accumulated arrogance of a man who had made cuckolds (this was far from being the case, for he had emerged out of a past barren as Crusoe's as far as passionate attachments went). Would she care to join him in a drink? Would she? Nothing daunted, she gave him one quick look and said:

'Very well, thank you. I think I could.'

With some such preliminaries their life together had begun: in smoke, uproar and the sight of blood as if in the midst of a bombardment – to the skirl of a barrel-organ in the street outside and the look of incomprehension on his face (for he knew not a word of the language), while she chattered away in German.

They left arm in arm at closing time. He informed her that he had thrown up his profession and gone to seek his fortune on the continent of Europe. Morose and unsettled, he wore the air of a conspirator passing through enemy territory at night (although everything about him suggested furtive though arrested flight – a figure of doom superimposed on the landscape in dramatic photogravure). Plunged in a gloom out of which no succour could hope to lift him, Alpin the versatile Bachelor of Arts was twelve years her junior.

They set up house together in Newton Road, Paddington. Her forthright manner both perturbed and enchanted him. He himself had attempted to expand his hopes by the guarded necessity of having innumerable alternatives and had almost succeeded in abolishing them altogether. In the following summer they crossed to Dublin. They were seen at the Horse Show where Sevi's curious manner of dressing was noticed by the press, her photograph appearing in the next morning's newspaper over the caption: 'Miss S. Klein, a visitor from Cologne, photographed in the jumping enclosure yesterday.' After that they moved to a hotel twenty miles down the coast, driving through the pass one evening in a hired car, hoisting their baggage onto the Grand Hotel counter and signing their false names with a flourish: 'Mr and Mrs Abraham Siebrito, Cascia House, Swiss Cottage, London, NW3.' There they came together at last steadfast as man and wife, though he was almost young enough to be her own long-lost son, and no marriage lines had ever been cried over them.

They lay together at night listening to the freight trains pulling through the tunnels, exchanging confidences. She spoke of a wet night at Enschede on the German–Dutch border. Woken in the early hours of the morning by bicycle bells and noises from the drunks in the lane behind the hotel, she had heard a monstrous voice roar with a blare almost of ordnance, and in English:

'Run! Run! Run from me! . . . But do not run in a circle!' He mentioned a Negro whom he had observed buying a newspaper outside the *S-Bahn* in Berlin, and how the action of selecting money from a reefer-jacket, dropping it into the vendor's box, taking a newspaper, thrusting it under his arm and entering the station, was performed to a rhythm almost ballad-like – a flowing series of poetic actions, he said, as appropriate as the equivalent in an uncorrupted com-

munity, performed with the 'rightness' of hundreds of years of repetition behind it; the same economical gestures he had seen put to another use on Inisheer when the islandmen were launching the currachs. Into a mechanical and self-conscious milieu the Negro had introduced something as natural and unexpected as the village pumps encountered among the chromium and neon signs on the Kurfürstendamm.

'But why not?' she said. 'After all, the Negro has been a city man since the invention of printing.'

'But not as a free man, Sevi,' he said. 'Not free.'

'Free?' said Sevi faintly, '*Herr Gott!* Who's free?'

Then she slept with her knees drawn up, drawing on oxygen as the dying draw on air. From such deep sleeps, recurring over and over again, light as sediment, heavy as evidence, she was not so much woken up as retrieved. He did not attempt to touch her, for there were depths into which he did not care to penetrate. Apprehensive of a bitterness and venom half perceived or guessed at beyond her habitual kindness, beyond her ability to be hurt, while he himself was attempting the impossible – to hold such contradictory elements together in his love. Every day he feared he would lose her, and every night he feared he was going to bed alone, seeing her bound so: the distress of a frontier people obliged to present their backs to grievance and opposition. About her hung an air of demolition; taking herself so much for granted she seemed immune to her own destruction. Her presence admitted no other alternative; she could only be relieved when she was let go. Since he held the scales in his hand, perhaps he felt also that she was disappointed in him. Looking for an arena where she could be put away, she had not found it in his cold bed. Even though his love was offered *in extremis*. Even though he was himself invaded and all his neutrality violated.

She went for long walks alone; returning late at night, re-entering the sleeping village, coming to the hotel where her lover lay sleeping. As she ascended the stairs the building seemed to shake, so that he awoke to become the unborn child in her womb, and the whole resounding hotel her stomach. She stood outside the door listening before taking the handle in her hands and tearing it open. He started up in bed. Standing with the light behind her she hissed into the dark bedroom:

'*Michael, bist du aufgewacht?* . . . *Ich bin zurückgekommen.*'

Sevi chain-smoked everywhere, taking volumes of Proust into dinner, dining on prawns. Rain kept them indoors for days on end, arguing on the stairs; she went out only to exercise her dachshund, Rosa Flügel, or to attend Mass. She came down to dinner in a housecoat of faded blue denim such as greengrocers favour, ate rapidly, reading from a book propped up before her, arranging prune stones in an absent manner on the cloth. He loved and desired her, incapable of the most rudimentary caution. He felt a tension in her which would not permit her to age – holding her years like a pendant about a no-longer-young neck. Thus she came to invoke for him the incautious women of the eighteenth century, talented yet promiscuous, half whore, half wife. Thinking of Sevi he remembered Madame de Warens, and made himself participator in what he had lost. When he touched her flesh it seemed infested with another life. Sevi too was a woman never at rest, so that intimacy with her seemed hardly possible; she had travelled all her life and would probably continue to do so until the day of her death – his own intervention swept aside; so that she would always be out of reach. If sleep and death, as we are told, bestow on us a 'guilty immunity', then travel does too, for the traveller is perpetually in the wrong context; and she was such a traveller. Sevi Klein belonged by right to that unfortunate line of women found in history (and almost extinct in their own time) which its progress, in an unreasonable search for attitudes, abuses; at least there was a certain melancholy in her eye which suggested she was part of such an abuse. 'Unrelated' in the way that the sentiment 'Pray for the Donor' in churches is unrelated to the disorder of death itself and to the imminent horrors of the *Ewigkeit,* or to any condition such sentiments affected to cover, one waited in vain for the 'real' Sevi to appear. She smiled no reassuring modern smile but now and then produced a rare and archaic one of her own, a smirk that unpeopled the world. Sometimes the expressions so calmly uttered by her in the English tongue contained inaccuracies open to the widest interpretation; and towards these breaches in the walls of common usage his fears were constantly running, without, however, ever being able to close the gap. An act of revenge for her threatened to be a clumsy and unusually indelicate operation. Sooner or later in all her own undertakings wild flaws appeared, disorderly and complete. Gored by the bull of Roman Catholicism she had once made a pilgrimage to the Holy City, where an ardent male citizen had attempted to assault her indecently in a prominent position on Santa Scala, in the course of Passion Week ceremonies.

She had only to think, 'Now I have something extraordinary in my hands,' for the object, no matter what it was, to collapse on her. She said:

'In Paris it was like this – I thought that I was going to faint outside the Musée Grévin. The brightness of the streets had made me dizzy. I tried to ask for a glass of water in a shop there, but I couldn't make myself understood; they gave me a box of matches instead. Every day I passed that place they came out to laugh at me.'

No, she knew nothing of the larger resources and confounding quality of female tears, and thus could sneer in character:

'*Verliebte lieben es, in Gewahrsam genommen zu werden.*' Of her no timid lover need ask, beg:

'Am I debauching you, or are you debauching me?' because as a young girl she had already spared him that embarrassment. '*Wir glauben nicht an die Legende von uns selbst weil sie im Entstehen ist . . .*'

Justice hardly seemed to apply to her, her own nature not being porous enough, or lacking the space, the safe margin, for a change of heart, or for forgiveness.

From the beginning their relationship had proceeded erratically in a series of uncalculated rejections. She could be relied upon to say:

'Look, I haven't changed,' – as if this justified her as a

31

'woman in love' instead of condemning her as an out-and-out imposter. It was as though she must live a little ahead of herself, in the condition of having to be continually aroused out of her absence. It was true also that Sevi still escaped him. Another damp morning would begin, day breaking wretchedly, and without many preliminaries she would stand before the window, looking out on the sodden and discoloured earth, thinking her own thoughts. Both beaches lay deserted; gulls were collected over them, veering about, crying. The scavengers were collecting muck on the foreshore where Sevi had bathed naked. Her impatient form, damp hair and piteous skin! That part of me that is not me, in the person of another. There in a dream he had embraced her.

She crept back into bed beside him without a word and soon was asleep again. As he too began to sleep he was advancing into her, and advancing was troubled by a dream.

In the dream – in the dream! Hastening along the road among a crowd of pilgrims – never fast enough! Dreaming, he heard real cries coming from the rear, and blows. The pilgrims were taking to the ditches. He flung himself in among them and found his hands fastened on a woman's skirts. He was a child. Someone was passing, but it was forbidden to look. The pilgrimage to the queen was interrupted because she was coming in person on the road, hell for leather among her entourage. Power was passing, shaking the air. From the ditches on either side the bolder spirits were peering, whispering. He uncovered his head and looked.

At the level of his eyes and striding away from him down the crown of the road he saw a heavily built woman dressed in a transparent raincoat worn open like a cloak, above it a bald pate. In the ditches they were whispering in astonishment among themselves. Then the dream carried him abruptly forward into the town.

In the last part of the dream all were dispersing from the town rapidly, as though threatened. He found himself, adult now, hurrying out hand-in-hand with a girl who was unknown to him. The town was under shell-fire but the queen and her court had to remain behind. In great fear for himself, he felt the ground shift under his feet and his heart race as though to outstrip the danger. But the first shell was already airborne. He sensed it coming through the clouds of dust raised ahead of him by the feet of the pilgrims. It exploded up ahead in the crowd. He plunged on – almost racing now – hoping that the next would pass over his head. The smoke of the first explosion came drifting back, and as he went forward into it he sensed, low and directed, the dropping trajectory of the second. Then he saw it. Silently, almost casually, a white object was lobbing towards him, gathering speed as it turned down. Too late already he flung up his arms. The shell crashed through the walls of his chest, firing itself point-blank into his soft unmilitant heart. Localized and unhinged his last soundless yell went up. A blinding detonation followed, casting him out of sleep.

He awoke trembling in the grey light. Beside him Sevi huddled lifeless. He touched her; she groaned once and turned over. Incurable, incurable! So it would continue until all the charts of the body were stowed away, the record of its blood and its thinking completed, and the light of the eyes extinguished. He felt then as he or another might feel at the hour of death when the loathing borne by the suffering flesh goes out like a sigh to the objects the dying person stares at, and all the refuse collected together by that person in a lifetime brought up to date, stamped with a formal seal (corruption itself) and made part of the universal collection; so that the disgust with the Self, total and languishing no more, is transmitted to inanimate objects – sinless as well as free in space and time – and the dead person freed at last from the responsibility of feeling.

II

The coast road entered the hills beyond Shanganagh, climbing in the half-dark between cedar and eucalyptus. In the light again, houses appeared, designed like citadels and displaying Italian names. Built into the granite above the beach, they gazed without expression over the bay. The beach resembled a sand quarry converging on a sea. Semi-naked bathers descended wooden steps on its blind side, going down and shutting from sight the mock-Italian frontage, balconies and awnings, the chorus of eucalyptus trees.

They came on the coast train in the season, appearing first on the horizon in the most purposeful and heroic shapes, the women numerous and always protesting. Crowds of them lay on the shore all day in extraordinary attitudes of repose, while from above more and more were descending with the measured tramp of the damned. No wind disturbed the incoming sea or the prostrate people, and in the glare all that could be delineated was destroyed. Shore and sea merged, dog and clown were swallowed up in inextinguishable fire. On the high stanchions of the tea-rooms the bearded John Player sailor was burning, remote and lugubrious in hammered tin.

So the days drew out, tides entering and leaving, the heat continuing, the floating bodies aimless and inert on the water. Time appeared as a heavy hand giving or taking their life away, falling anyway, impartially on sand, on feeble walls, on tired summer trappings. And the smoke going straight up from the stands; and the children crying (a sound blood-dimmed and heavy to the ear, as though conducted there not by the air itself but by brass or copper); and the damp elders prone everywhere. For Saturday had come again and Saturday's tired population was at the sea.

All who arrived at the beach from sloblands and city – the deposed kings and queens of Torrent Hill, the bands of nuns released for the day from *L'Ordre des Ombres*, the Old Oak Infant Orphanage, the hooligans from Zoar Street – came shaken with a suspended summer lust, to hold a commemorative service on the summer passing and the free days. Submitting to chance freedom but performing the act diffidently and as though enacting a scene obviously 'beyond' them. A company coming down resigned, without too much enthusiasm and without too much style, into the Promised Land. The bulk, unconcerned with fair play, knowing in its bones the awfulness of any dealing, lay claim to their territory as graveyards lay claim to the dead. So these citizens were to claim this beach, lying there like an army fallen amidst its baggage; ground mollifying them, taking them into its secret at last, completing them. Admitting at the same time that under the name of 'hospitality' is concealed various disorders; heavy bodies saying in effect, *This is our ground; let us exploit it* (the resources of a spirit seldom fired conceiving only this drear Heaven of abject claims). So they descended in an uneven line all through summer, no individual shape an heroic shape any longer, but all the shape of the common plural.

One evening a member of the *lazzaroni* appeared on the beach. Destitute and unwhole, escaped from the tenements, he had made his way out of the station, dressed in an ancient overcoat which reached below the knees, found the steps, and arrived. The bay water was dead calm; an odour of eucalyptus hung in the air. The young ladies who had come from the hill convent were just collecting themselves together, preparing to leave. He had watched them from his perch, unseen and pawing himself doubtfully, without ever taking his eyes away. Spread below him he saw an intoxication of green uniforms and then a flurry of undressing, and then bare flesh, then girls shouting and swimming, and now dressed again and going. While the face hung above them, chalk-white where paralysis had killed it, the bleak jaw-line and the bared teeth presented as component sections of the human skull, the profound bone base of all emotion glaring back its final indifference. The freak face stared down, motionless and cold, negligent as features gouged in putty, with a stare which took in the area and destroyed it – the observer himself lost somewhere between unrelated head and unrelated body. Confronted with this all would be left in doubt, waiting for the final kindness to put it right or the final unkindness to annihilate it. The bay water remained calm; smoke rose blue in the air from the cooking stands; the nuns, careening themselves at a decent remove, were showing an emancipated leg on the feast-day of St James the Greater.

Nuns apart, the people were to become aware of him as

they might have become aware of the stench, the effluvium, which surrounds and yet contains discarded and putrefying matter. Not deformed in any striking manner, there remained something foul about his person, an uncertain wavering line drawing him down and compelling him to be recognized. They were looking at an imbecile, one of themselves, a person loose and lost, a young fellow in his mid-twenties – a 'fact' in the way a multiple exposure in photography is a fact, something irregular yet perfect, perfect yet a mechanical abuse of itself. Beyond that he was nothing, could be nothing, for there was nothing left over, no place where they, weeping with solicitude, could put their hands and say, 'This at least is ours.' He was like something they could not recollect. He was a disturbance in their minds. The normally healthy, when their health breaks down, speak of being 'in poor shape'; but he, who had seldom been healthy and never been normal, was poor shape incarnate. He was the Single One, a neuter.

A tenement child had lured him to ground level with her sly eyes, with a movement of her head which was partly a delicate soliciting and partly that dumb invitation we tender a beast. He crept out after her, the child turning and grinning, spilling water from her shining can. So he found himself among the people at last.

He began wandering about, head shaking and feet uncertain – a nameless fear. A tall and disjointed figure fashioned by all manner of winds, whose every movement was apprehensive, trailing his wake of misery behind. His stare lacked momentum, falling short of the object before he could 'take it in', painfully slow hands closing on the dog's head after the animal had moved, closing on air. His touch was more an experiment than an act of possession. The eyes he turned on them were dark and liquid, barbicans in his shattered face, guarded and half closed like the identical crenels of a tower: that old and wary perspective of eyes behind which the senses stood armed and uneasy – a minute suspicious stir in the wall's face. None could pity, or deplore or 'place' him because he could not be found, cound not find himself, lost and swallowed up by a continual and fobidding silence. No way remained open to remind him of a former disturbance which he could have gone back to and reclaimed – as a dog draws back its fangs from the security of the kennel, so this creature was drawing back from the appropriating touch on the arm which would identify him as a poor blind man. His feet were the first to despair, dragging the shadow, shadow in its turn flinching from the out-stretched 'charitable' hand. He was struck at such a pitch of intensity that he had to be heard to the end.

Those who were leaving made to pass him, but in their embarrassment wheeled round to face him, at a loss and unhappy, clutching at their possessions and saying to their children:

'Come along now . . . oh now come along!' not even knowing where to look any more. Then he covered his face, churning in the sand, cancelling himself with his own hand. The shadows on the cabins were locked together for an instant and then wrenched apart. They did not wish to see him or be witness to this distress, for among them he was an effigy and a blasphemy, something beyond the charity of God or man. Perishing so in his own presence, he seemed to be devouring himself. Existing outside perspective, he could not be considered as an equivalent to themselves.

Thrown out of order and at a loss the herd was in full retreat, their dreadful faces turned about, their mouths wailing soundlessly. And then nothing. Silence fell. He went alone through it, ignored. Their silence, no longer a retreat, became an intermission – a trying situation out of which all hoped presently to advance, voluble and unrepentant, back into the good life out of which all had been cast. Presented with this figure of doom their Christian feelings had fled. Here was no blind man, only one who did not care to remember; this patient brought no dreams to the session.

And so, little by little, life returned and darkness fell. All the living were out and about as though nothing had happened, blown hither and thither by the high winds of commiseration, holding aloft their stupendous banners, being obliging, running messages (their obligations running before, to rob them), being spiteful. Spiteful!

Hin-und her gerissen! . . . *Schweinfieber!* Save the patronage of their kind names. They went down blind into the dark pool, the shadows falling everywhere and the ending never likely. They went down. Dark clouds were forming overhead. Look here! Look there! Unkind life is roaring by in its topmost branches.

III

The late summer when he had watched that had gone for good. Now it was winter: late evening-time in an Irish October. The short winter day was drawing to an end. He sat on the sea wall and watched her tramping along the bluff, heralded by some piteous cries from some climbing goats. She came trailing into sight after a while, crossing below, barefooted, trailed by her low German hound; she resembled a person who never intended to come back. He watched her, a dark blur by the water's edge, her shoulders were moving. He leant forward (could she be crying?) and saw she was writing with a stick on the sand, the palimpsest. '*Das ist des Pudels*,' she wrote, and below that one word, '*Kern*,' in a crabbed backhand. That was that. The tired eye had begun to close; soon they could go to their various ways. It was not as if light had been drained from the sand but as if darkness had been poured into it. Now almost invisible he sat aloft so that Sevi came for the last time, walking slowly against the sea and against the last light, penetrating him as an oar breaks water. But not stopping, retreating, descending stairs of sand, going out slowly followed by the dog. He watched her evaporating, crawling into her background, not declining it, deliberately seeking it, lurching away from him to stumble into a new medium (a way she had), beating down the foreshore like a lighter going aground. Her hair undone went streaming back from her head; for an instant longer she remained in sight, contracting and expanding in the gloom, and then was gone.

The tide rose now until it covered the entire shore. Shallow yet purposeful water embraced the extremity of the sea wall. Invisible gulls were complaining, worrying, somewhere over its dark unpeaceful depths. Anxiously the pier lights waved a mile to the south – a remote outfall of light more dingy than the sky, now dropping, now drowned in intervening wave. Michael Alpin walked out of the dark construction of the wall, broken here and there by heavy seas. He stood over her scrawlings, her last abuse. Unbuttoning himself he took his stance staring out to sea, his lust or love in the end reduced to this. Retreating to the wall he laid his face against its intolerable surface of freezing stone. As he began to go down the false surf light and the remote light along the pier, diminishing, swung away.

There is no commencement or halfway to that fall: only its continuing.

Sodden Fields

1985/1989

Monday 3 March 1930. A thick pearl grey blue day; water drops on the window . . . The sun wells up, like a pulse, behind the clouds. Tremendous shoals of birds are flying, and the flop eared trains meeting as usual under Caburn.

The Diary of Virginia Woolf

Vain gaiety, vain battle, vain repose,
Themes of the embittered heart, or so it seems . . .

W. B. Yeats, 'The Circus Animals' Desertion'

1
1927
Earliest Misgivings; the March of the Cadavers

Is it the sole, that strange denizen of the deep, a lurker on sea-beds, that (out of curiosity about the hook) *catches itself*? Unless I am confusing sole with plaice, or monk, or flounder.

Be that as it may, I was born on the third day of March in the year 1927 in the old Barony of Salt in the County Kildare in the Province of Leinster, of lapsed Catholic parents since deceased, under the watery astrological sign of Pisces.

A fresh westerly airstream covered most areas while a frontal trough of low pressure remained stationary over Ireland but seemed about ready to move eastward.

Conceived at the tail-end of an early June day, in the Year of Grace 1926, I was expelled the following March 3rd, passing over into 1927 puffing and choking with mouth half open, the cold without being so intense, wellnigh irresistible the compulsion to sink back into the warmer uterine depths with a bubbling groan.

Hearing faraway music, moody themes from the good-times-gone: Albinoni's now-famous *Adagio* or a Debussy *Arabesque* played on the harp. Not yet the wild nocturnal bagpipe music and the night wind tipping the pans of the weighing-scales as they filled with rainwater on the bedroom windowsill of a bungalow in Emor Street just off the South Circular Road in the so-called Liberties in the city of Dublin. This would be in the late seventies when I was the ill-dressed recipient of a most welcome cheque for $7,000 from the American-Irish Foundation – Kennedy bad-conscience money paid out on sole condition that I reside for ten months in my erstwhile homeland, which I had not been in a position to afford since leaving it twenty-five years before.

43

A group of young lady harpists from New York, all of surpassing comeliness, were entertaining the American ambassador, Mr Shannon, and his lovely wife and their selected guests after lunch in the US representative's fine residence in the Phoenix Park. A herd of grazing deer was visible through the elegant long windows as Ambassador Shannon, bald as a coot though a decade younger than the shabby recipient, handed over a sealed envelope. Held in close-up for Irish television viewers to admire, it was seen to be clearly addressed to Seamus Heaney, the previous year's winner.

I had just turned fifty.

All this by way of preamble. Nothing is too clear, of its nature, least of all the limpidities of language, the particles of which must be 'clear as sand'. The strange phosphorus of life, nameless under the old misappellation.

I tell you a thing. I could tell it otherwise. A few pictures emerge into the light from the shadows within me. I consider them. Quite often they fail to please me. I call them 'pictures' but you, kind readers, ideal readers suffering from an ideal insomnia, must know otherwise. What I mean to convey is: *movements from the past.*

So, putting as bold a face on it as I could under the circumstances, out I crawled yelling blue bloody murder, roughly handled by a wet-nurse from Cavan.

Why, there are days when we do not know ourselves, when we do not properly belong to ourselves, as children know to their cost. Assailed by mysterious sundowns and gory red endings of days: the extraordinary clarity of the nocturnal firmament burning above the little pier on Annaghvaughan and the unmilked cattle bawling in descant. Then out went the candle and we were left darkling. Breathe in, breathe out. In the memory of old men it's always June. But were the summers of my childhood as sunny as I seem to recall?

In that Year of Our Lord nineteen hundred and twenty-seven, Coole Park was taken over by the Land and Forestry Commission in Co. Galway. In America, at Bridgewater

44

Penitentiary, Sacco and Vanzetti walked to the electric chair. Flying out over the Atlantic in the dark, the intrepid Colonel Lindbergh landed near Paris in the dark. In Berlin the ageing lecher Frank Harris was lecturing on Shakespeare. Kevin O'Higgins, our first diplomat, returning home from Mass, was murdered outside his own front gate. In a public ward of St Patrick Dun's Hospital in Dublin, the Countess Markievicz died of peritonitis. Long insane and widowed sixty years, the Empress Carlotta passed quietly away quietly in Belgium.

The lost *mediodesorientado* Hugo von Hofmannstahl died in Vienna. In Paris the long-demented Baroness Elsa von Freytag-Loringhoven gassed herself, the baron having taken his own life just before the outbreak of the Great War. In Paris the American novelist Djuna Barnes with her lover Thelma Wood, the silverpoint artist from Missouri, were looking after the richly left Natalie Clifford Barney's garden in the rue Jacob, a patch of earth that had formerly belonged to Racine. Tea and special little cakes were served up there in the temple dating from just before the French Revolution; tall Thelma the infected carrier of the past, the born *somnambule*, the bitch of all time, turning up as 'Robin Vote' in the 1936 novel *Nightwood*; Djuna Barnes was 'Nora Flood'. Their anguished avatars were quarrelling in the apartment with the wooden horse and heavy liturgical decorations, the ill-fitting purple dress and shapeless Napoleonic hat, on the fifth floor of number 9 rue St-Romain, going out to get thoroughly pickled at the Flore.

It was the year that Alice Prin (Kiki of Montparnasse), the mistress of Man Ray the Dada artist and photographer, had an exhibition of her paintings at Galerie du Sacre du Printemps.

While from Kenosha, a town on Lake Michigan on the Wisconsin shore, Richard Ives Welles was committed by his father into Kankee State Institution for the Insane. Stuttering Dick had been the laughing-stock of the Kenosha cornerboys. In Cuba that summer his precociously gifted younger brother George Orson was on vacation with his guardian, the shifty Dr Bernstein.

All this occurred in 1927, the year of the long count in the

Dempsey–Tunney world heavyweight fight, the year when de Valera began the even longer *völkisch* reign of Fianna Fáil. Hand in glove with the cultural nationalism proper to those peerless warriors of yore: our own élite dead long gone to their reward, the Fainna Eireann.

In 1927, a year after the first staging of Sean O'Casey's play *The Plough and the Stars*, the playwright married Eileen Reynolds, a pretty actress twenty-three years younger than himself.

Do you hear me now?

Are we not all somebody's rearings in the wretched bric-à-brac and rigmarole of history, of which our life may be assigned some part, however minor, if only as passive bystander?

In that Year of Grace 1927, Sylvia Townsend Warner's novel *Mr Fortune's Maggot* came out in London. Vipers appear, earthworms engender, forward turnips rot and toads crawl forth every year in March. 'It is the period *just before oneself*, the period of which in earliest days one knew the actual survivors, that really lays a strong hand upon one's heart.' I must have read it somewhere.

In 1927 young Clarence Malcolm Lowry was homeward bound aboard the SS *Pyrrhus* from the Far East with a mixed cargo of wild beasts and crawling reptiles, an elephant, five black panthers, ten snakes, a wild boar, all trapped in the Straits Settlements and now consigned to lifelong captivity in the Dublin zoo, to be cared for by Superintendent Flood. Where presently, shivering all over like a dog, I would be lifted up by my nanny, in order to offer a banana to Lowry's elephant, or rather to a long, feeling, prehensile trunk that blew on me a gust of wildness, unknown terrain, swamps, a scorching sun. Taken by Nanny to see the wild animals, I was struck by the untamed sulphurous stink of the lion house, hardly less by the rude monkey house, the elephant house, the giraffe house. Cracked semi-human voices spoke out from the fidgety macaws in the parrot house, their plumage the colour of fire and blood, of red rage trapped in a hothouse, humming, lurid, obscene. These fraught excursions to the grey city with its own peculiar and (for me) disturbing smells would always end with a spell of vomiting.

'The lad's over-excited,' my parents agreed.

Henry Williamson's *Tarka the Otter* was published in 1927, to be read aloud to me by my mother some years later. Joseph-Napoléon Primoli died that year. Between receiving the Nobel Prize in 1925 and publishing *The Intelligent Woman's Guide to Socialism and Capitalism*, the spry septuagenarian and vegetarian George Bernard Shaw, social reformer and patron of the Life Force, dogmatic busybody and former vestryman and borough councillor who had several times raised the question of women's toilets for St Pancras and tried to organize a crematorium there, had turned seventy-one. Instantly recognizable everywhere thanks to his tweedy knickerbockers and long argumentative beard, he had been around since 1856, seemingly the same frail Elderly Protestant Irish Gent all his natural life. He had twenty-three more useful years of postcard-writing to total strangers, when not pottering about the garden at Ayot St Lawrence. Captious, he had an answer for everything, liked to put philosophers in their place, dined on raw vegetables, milk, hardboiled eggs. He wanted to dazzle, to confound.

In the same year America drew up secret military plans for war against Great Britain. Against Winter, chess grandmaster Capa made insolent moves standing up, hardly bothering to sit down and think.

Legend had it that grandmaster Paul Morphy died in his bath surrounded by women's shoes. It was not long before Alekhine gave up alcohol, switched to milk and trounced Dr Max Euwe (1901–81) to hold the world chess title for the next two years, a decade before *Guernica*. In Trinity College, Dublin, a Bachelor of Arts degree was conferred upon Samuel Barclay Beckett.

In 1927 King Ferdinand I of Romania, the second Hohenzollern king, died of cancer of the bowel in Bucharest. Abel Gance's epic movie *Napoléon* was released; the talkies began in Hollywood. Micheál MacLiammóir left the Slade and joined the touring company of his brother-in-law,

47

Anew MacMaster. In Dublin the O'Nolan family, formerly of Tyrone, moved from Herbert Place to Blackrock. Virginia Woolf's novel *To the Lighthouse* was published by the Hogarth Press. Hammond of Gloucestershire scored a thousand runs in May, at Southampton against Hampshire.

On August 6th a London insurance clerk called Edward Harry ('Ed') Temme swam the freezing English Channel from Cap Grisnez to Lydden Spout, using the trudgeon stroke. Helen Wills Moody won the ladies' singles in the first of her record eight victories at Wimbledon. Anne Yeats, W. B.'s little daughter, put a squeaky cushion on a chair for Lady Gregory to sit upon; Her Ladyship was not amused.

It was the year of '*la generación de 1927*' in Madrid, with Lorca, Alberti, Altolaguirre, Cernude, José Bergamin and Pedro Garfias meeting to talk and foment dissension in the Café Gijon, the Granje del Henar, the Café Castilla, the Fornos, Kutz, Café de la Montaña, Café Pombo where Raymon de la Serna held court every Saturday night; Buñuel, Dali and Pepín Bello were in the Casa de Leonor, a brothel on the Calle de la Reine.

In the spring of that year, V. S. Pritchett had set out from London to walk across western Spain from Badajoz to León, a hundred-mile hike in heavy winter tweeds, on foot and alone. In Berlin the shifty Brecht, a lifelong womanizer, parted company with Marianne Brecht, née Zoll, to take up with his future wife Helene Weigel. Gunter Grass was born in Danzig, hereinafter Gdansk, Poland.

In 1927 T. S. Eliot was received into the Anglo-Catholic faith at St Stephen's church opposite the Russian Orthodox Church in Exile, not far from the Round Pond in Kensington where W. B. Yeats as a boy had sailed his fancy toy yacht.

In June of that year the Woolfs had witnessed an eclipse of the sun from a moor in north Yorkshire ('The earth was dead,' Virginia recorded in her diary). The next eclipse would be in 1999.

In that year Buckminster Fuller, the Harvard man who had invented the geodesic dome, gave up earning a living, stopped talking for two years. Ernst Lubitsch made *In Old Heidelberg*, a silent movie version of Romberg's operetta *The*

Student Prince. Hollywood films were shown in the stables off the cobbled courtyard at Oakley Park. My younger brother and I sucked bull's-eyes and marvelled at the G-men. The villagers craned forward on kitchen chairs, guffawed at Leon Errol.

In 1933, when I would have turned six, the Liffey flooded the village up as far as Marley Abbey. The flood came out through the open forge door and the houses seemed all set to sail away.

March 3rd in Basho's day was the Festival of the Dolls in sixteenth-century Japan: *hina matsuri*, sometimes called the Festival of Pearl Blossoms. Or simply Girls' Festival, which would suit me fine, backing into the strange withdrawn world of the fish. The Piscean twilight world of the deep fish lost, or just gone astray in the head. Is this why the light still enchants me, the hidden observer remaining a prey to the most giddy kind of guilt? But now, classic-lovers, it's diddley-diddley time once again.

Fifty was Basho's age when with failing health he began that long last marathon hike into south Japan in 1694. He was six years junior to Jane Bowles – if you'd kindly be good enough to move on three centuries – when she died in a hospital in Málaga, capital of sorrow. In a snail-bar near the brothel quarter the shabby ghost of Terry Butler of Shanganagh, never so shabby in life, failed to recognize me, darkened by tramping in the Sierra Almijara.

Who am I? Am I or am I not the same person I have always taken myself to be? In that case, who am I? Is the silence significant or just lack of something to say? Is that significant? Speak up, but kindly confine yourself to essentials; write on one side of the paper only.

Where am I? Where was I then? What do you do when memory begins to go? I spend much of the time looking back into the past. It is no longer there. It has moved. Where to?

The city certainly had changed. The Grafton Picture House was closed, turned into a bingo arcade, the ghosts in the toilet departed, the commissionaire Mr Shakespear dead. It was still raining in that most mournful thoroughfare called Aungier Street, on the offices of Fanagan the undertaker, the busiest man in Dublin.

Meanwhile, then, up in his fine new residence in Rathfarnham, Senator William Butler Yeats, impaled upon a fine idea, was just looking at his yellow canaries and saw symbols streaming. Moving to his writing-desk in a dream he seated himself, drew out his day-book, wrote in his distinguished calligraphy: 'I am a crowd. I am a lonely man. I am nothing.' Whereupon all the canaries started singing.

He did not care to name his enemies as such when corresponding with fine ladies, Irish and English, but designated them thus: The Wolf Dog, The Harp, The Shamrock, The Tower. And (rather finely) Verdis-Green Sectaries.

Senator Willie was his father's son and no two ways about it. The correspondence with his father is nothing less than heart-warming, and not something you expect in such close blood connections. James Joyce was still working on the scaffolding of the *Wake* in sinful Paris. Mr Beckett had just written: 'The sun shone, having no alternative, on the nothing new.' The sharp-faced student Brian Ó Nuallain was refusing to learn bad Irish from his professor, Douglas Hyde, later to be President of Ireland; he whom David Thomson saw crawling on all fours across a drawing-room with a bar of chocolate protruding from his mouth below the walrus moustache, challenging some well-brought-up little colleens to take a bite; he too perhaps impaled upon a dream.

In Kinsale great hauls of mackerel were taken; three fish-girls sea-salting and packing per barrel, cutting and stowing the catch for the cooper to come and tack down the barrels which were then rolled along the pier.

The Wall Street Crash was imminent.

2
1987
Battle and Aftermath; the Beast of Ballynagrumoolia

If the wholesale slaughter that was the Battle of Kinsale finished off the rough princely world of Latinists and gallowglasses in three hours in the Ballinamona bog, had it not been lost already when McMahon sold out O'Neill in return for a bottle of the hard stuff on that miserable wet late December day 387 years ago? No?

Neap tides flooded 9,288 times into Ballymacus Creek where as a difficult young thing you liked to retire, to sulk. Our independence won with jigs and reels God knows how many church collections later, and the national flag raised jerkily aloft in mismatching shades of dandelion orange (leaves, stalk and root containing a bitter milky juice) and septic green, divided by neutral white, and complemented by a national anthem that was never any great shakes, 'composed' by a north Dublin housepainter, a bowsy by the name of Carney reputedly related to the roistering Behans.

Years later, out walking with you on another soft December day beyond the ramparts, we spotted the Beast of Ballynagrumoolia beyond a denuded winter hedge. Pale and plump, the deep-set piggish eyes red-rimmed like an anus, the flaccid cheeks soiled with mud, immemorial slobber, shit and tears. The Beast's stiff yellow hair was erupting from under nodding headgear, fore-hooves rooting in the driveway, the twin enraged nostrils aflare; while from the deep barrel chest stormily rising and subsiding came grievous sighs and the most heartfelt groans. Great sods of earth were being hurled about; an apparition as alarming as a she-gorilla enraged – the very stuff of nightmares.

Scavengers, looters and pillagers, the extreme poor of Munster arrived with the wild dogs and birds of prey to cover

51

the battlefields now become graveyards, a thousand of O'Neill's and O'Donnell's men become shades, in an unforgettable day that would be for Ireland what Kossovo would be for Hungary. But the poison was already being prepared and the wild geese scattered, soon to become extinct. Something was broken so that something else could begin.

And sure enough, scarcely had a year passed than there came yet another in the long roster of our betrayal; this one by the name of Jamsey Blake, turncoat and native of Galway who was said to be in the pay of Sir George Carew the Lord High President of Munster. It was he who arranged that poison be laid out for Red Hugh at a dinner in Simancas, watched him sample wine of the Palomino grapes, swig and swallow; take *percebes*, which are goose barnacles, now stuffed with death, take his portion with a slow easy hand. Blake, hidden, watched, and so did some ruffed and bearded Spanish grandees, not comprehending; saw him swallow it in a place now outside of time, wiped out by time, frozen within time.

As the Scots troops crouched miserably all night in cornstooks in freezing rain, their powder damp, their spirits low, awaiting Cromwell's fearful attack at sun-up, time stopped. At daybreak the Scots troops began shuffling into line.

Elsewhere in other times and places in different darkness St Elmo's fire was glinting on damp Irish lances (not to be used much that day) and Panzer tank engines coughing into life at sun-up were rolling towards Kusk. These fields, Kossovo and its crows, the tank battle of Kusk, the graveyard of Kinsale, a drenched cornfield in Scotland. *Jamais deux sans trois*; never four without more.

Shrapnel tore through the grey insentient air, bees with their hives knocked over. From the enemy lines the machine-gun fire was reaching out, stuttering, probing, stitching the air. Somewhere in the murk ahead lay the pierced barbed-wire entanglements. Juss trod on something soft and yielding – flayed human flesh not yet dead, himself dragged along by the current of time. His face felt stiff as a death-mask, from generous tots of three-star Hennessy. The thought flew unsoberly through his head: *Schicksal* had become *Schnicksal*, both British and Germanic destiny become ridiculous and dirty, become piercing red-hot. The ordinary expection of suffering was one thing; this was something else again.

The Beast of Ballynagrumoolia had come via Ballinspittle through all the intervening gardens of Munster, breaking down clapboard fences, trampling vegetable patches, grunting and sweating, to Kippagh.

The Battle of Kinsale was fought and lost one vile wet Sunday on the 24th of December 1601 and over in barely three hours. Within a period so brief a large force was destroyed by a smaller one, the English horse under Wingfield pursued the fleeing Irish as far as Innishannon five miles distant, killing at will. The Spanish presence within the town had been more a hindrance than a help. Trust not foreign friends; the old adage had a cruel ethnic twist to it. The River Bandon snaked about the small port, a walled town of two hundred houses, as duodenum and colon, lower bowel and anus. Spared the shame of defeat, the Spanish were flushed down the river and out to sea. Don Juan del Aquila was in command. The Armada had sunk only thirteen years before. For the Irish, crippling defeats at the Yellow Ford and Benburb, and now Kinsale, the final setback. The ancestors had begun to seem strange. *Kolkrabe the Raven greets you!* Shaking out sodden feathers, stropping its beak on the bars of the cage. Hiding its food, first under this stone, then under that. Swearing profusely, e'er all be over and done with. Ever since the sixteenth century the wind had been blowing against European Catholicism.

Our Jamesie O'Connor, a fifth- or sixth-generation bachelor, on the dole, impoverished and half mad, was as a lost creature struggling in a mangrove swamp. Still believing that his dead brother had been converted into a crow and out after him in all weathers in a long unchanged greasy overcoat in one pocket of which he kept his silent gun – a catapult.

He dwelt bachelor-style in a cramped and fetid one-room

Assumption Terrace cottage hard by the charitable fishmongers who fed him, opposite the Health Centre
('Pregnant? We can help') and the Garda station out of
which at any moment the opera-loving but ill-tempered
Guard Con Concannon might purposefully stride, demanding a licence for the silent gun, make him eat crow.

Insects too have their hour.

Jamesie's window overlooked the end of the ancient
Celtic world. He whittled at odds and ends to make a fire,
kept a mangy cat, preferred candles to newfangled notions
such as electric light, drank in The Harp and Shamrock,
where he was known as 'Whackers'. As with Wagner before
him, he suffered agonies from skin disease, piles and rotten
bladder, his memory shot to pieces. Irish to the core, his
temper uncertain, he wanted to kill the crow that was his
brother. The same old dingdong.

Out walking in winter, one memorable evening, we
encountered the Beast of Ballynagrumoolia at close
quarters, in all her glory. A dinted and holey aluminium
chamberpot was clamped down on the pointed skull and
fastened with a demi-veil of fishing-net knotted about the
throat in a loose fashion with brown scapulars contesting
with an Immaculate Conception badge on a faded crimson
thread; the white paint cracked on the chamber, the blue
rim chipped, and strapped about it (a daring touch) welder's
goggles. A scarf of pale green fruit-netting the colour of a
well-weathered copper church dome bisected the neck. And
from neck to ankle a kimono-like vestment of a nondescript
dull colour, a swaggered double skirt like a priest's cassock or
Franciscan's habit, at midriff a double length of hairy twine,
of the same colour as the hair erupting from under the
cracked chamber. This mottled black shapeless bolt of cloth
ended in battered brogans. Mad blue periwinkle eyes were
set in the middle of the 'face' implanted with an iron-hard
snout, for rooting in nameless filth. The deep-set eyes were
hidden and furtive, wedged into their sockets below the
fuzzy eyebrows; the corrugations of the narrow forehead
signalling God knows what itch, what fury, puzzlement,

54

betraying softly mimed buffoonery with a tug to tow-coloured hair, absented finger up one nostril, a quick tug at the hair wiry as tow, the snot examined and tasted, swallowed. And then stock still, ears cocked, listening hard, then relaxed, whereupon a deep rumbling fart to end this evening's performance. It was a she-beast assuredly to judge from the nauseating vegetable smell that wafted its way across the narrow roadway as we slunk by. Not our Queen Maeve as represented on the one-punt denomination note looking as woebegone as if she had a crippling pain in the hole, nor yet *Verfremdungseffekt* nor Bubba nor Maggie Humm, nor Banba nor Foohla the Flighty, nor Puckoon, nor the OldSowThatEatsHerFarrow, nor yet again Eman-rehsihtstahw, the lowly form of an immortal always encountered at that mystical hour 'twixt gloaming and dusk, as now. On all fours, face on fire, grovelling in the dirt.

We passed down the mossy boreen until we came to the main road leading in one direction to nowhere in particular, in the other by the house of hidden Jago and the otter path, then past the flowering cherry at the Carraigin corner and by the blind-factory to the marsh and its assembly of wild birds with their diverse cries, curlews and oystercatchers and plover and mallard, the heavenliness of birdsong that so enraptured W. H. Hudson on the pampas in Argentina in the nineteenth century, as the birds of Hampshire had delighted Gilbert White the Selbourne divine in the century before.

The trawler *Girl Fiona* was tied up at the World's End wharf near where the Cornishman 'mad' Mark Trick lived under a thatched roof with his ever-loving wife Lucinda (née Minogue) of the knockers. Her lord and master was playing loud *Magic Flute* music all night long on the transistor, having brought his dead mother safely from distant Cornwall in a coffin, set out upon the Harbour Bar counter, Mad Mark calling loudly for drinks on the house. And then the casket up-ended in a corner like a cello, then more drinks before burial in Courtaparteen cemetery, that old disused place near the deserted village.

Only dead fish swim with the tide. Our past is most

certainly dead. More than that, much more; it's unimaginable. Unthinkable as the legendary but extinct horseflesh Twohelochroo, or Boggeragh, or flighty Firbolg, or the Pooka, or Babh, or the mighty thundering hooves of The Morrigu herself.

Jackdaws nest in the limes of Friary Hill, tear twigs, lay eggs, raise young, drop eggshells and whiten with their squirted lime-shit the newly washed limousines lined up for Mass, strut about on the road. A robin calls 'Swing low, sweet chariot!' over by the French Prison and from near the slaughterhouse on Chairman's Lane a blackbird answers *'Aujourd'hui! Aujourd'hui!'* as the legless man is pushed in his wheelchair into a waiting car, and The Buck goes bounding down the narrow stairs and out into the freshness of Cork Street, jacket hooked over one finger, humming 'The Mountains of Mourne', released from rearranging that evergreen lament for his male voice choir.

Daybreak comes early in June to the port, with a bantam cock crowing lustily twenty-nine times, mongrels in the morning, the canoodling of pigeons, the tide coming into the town of ghosts (population 2,000); 1601 was but yesterday, and spooks abound. Joy-bells ring for living and drowned (the Irish life underneath the waves); when the tide goes out and the wind drops there'll be a couple of jumps.

A bitch on heat is being chased through the flat of town by six mongrels anxious to cover her, despite newly enacted bye-laws for the control of wandering pets; but ours was ever a country notoriously difficult to control. Windblown pines, surging ambient darkness.

Monsignor Cosimo Bumperini, SJ, Th.D., Ph.D., rotund and benign, a well-pleased ecclesiastical pumpkin, confidant to His Eminence the Cardinal Primate, the Papal Nuncio, having left Ardcarrig guest-house on Compass Hill (perhaps the most expensive B & B in Munster), strolled by Dr FitzGerald's ivy-covered wall, heading for the friary, murmuring his Nones.

Monsignor Bumperini's belly extended a good eighteen or

twenty centimetres in advance of the rest of him, the gooseberry-coloured eyes fairly starting from their sockets. Capillaries had erupted on his purple cheeks and small veins ruptured on his nose, testifying to liberal intake of more than just altar wine. His bulgy eyes looked craftily out behind the glint of spectacles. A seemingly kind man; not exactly a man of God, a self-promoting party who held himself in the highest esteem. The smile was misleadingly benevolent, more smirk than smile.

Gravely he saluted a bearded fellow in blue, Peter Storm, out walking with his darksome fancy-woman, now heading back to the Dutch House, a third-storey apartment under the eaves loud with the croodles and canoodling of amorous pigeons, hard by the French Prison.

The Jesuit father was over from Turin on an Irish visit and would dine that evening with Canon Norman Prior of St Multose in The Blue Haven, a favoured meeting-place of Protestants. Now he came upon a strange sight, to be sure.

A little hunchback friar with crooked teeth was ringing the Angelus. Light as a leaf in his brown habit he was lifted a good two or three feet off *terra firma* in his sandals at each energetic pull at the rope, to be followed presently by the resonant clang of the big bell on its stanchion firm as a guillotine, grim as a gallows; the friar ascending and descending with eely agility, grinning from ear to ear. Monsignor Bumperini thought of Quasimodo. Passing he gravely blessed the small unearthly airborne friar again rising on his rope.

'Such delightful serenity,' breathed the monsignor to himself, nodding to the again ascending diminutive friar at the end of his rope. The monsignor quickened his pace. At that moment all the lights sprang on in the Tap Tavern.

On the main dock before the Trident Hotel (long closed for repairs) the filthy German coaster *Eugen Rothenhoefer* out of Hamburg was offloading maize for Henry Good, and there a pair of far from polished peasants saluted us affably. Sick and tired of cooling their heels outside the Temperance Hall, Garr and his mate Paddy Locke had set out for a breath of fresh air by the river at the Archdeacon Duggan bridge. Not 'peasants of the cuntree' but fine upstanding fishermen of Kinsale and they lifelong buddies as inseparable as curds and whey. To ward off carnal desire they swore mighty oaths all the time, spitting, Paddy advancing crabwise in an indirect and shifty manner that had grown habitual with him when in his cups.

Paddy Locke devoured ox-hearts, sheeps' lights, eels and pike from the Bandon, calves' livers, pigs' crubeens, hedgehog and pigeon, saddle of hare, curlew breasts, Carrigaline duck, buck rabbit, salmon in and out of season from the drift nets, herring and crab, chanterelle and ceps from the damp Garretstown bluebell woods, free-range eggs, skate from the sea-bed off the Old Head, mussels from under seaweed on the rocks below the Dutch flats. All this to his heart's content, when he could keep it down. For his appetite for food as such was not great, his staple and preferred diet being draught Guinness in pint tumblers.

He perjured himself as the other fishermen did in the District Court on the ticklish subject of monofilament nets drifting for salmon out of season, a double illegality, contradicting stoutly all the water bailiff had seen or thought he had seen on the rocks, in the sea, pulling in, the coming and going, the dimmed lights, the covering and uncovering, who was carrying what where, all impossible to prove in a court of law. But, as is well known, fishermen from St Peter on were all notorious liars.

The lights were springing up all over Kinsale and evening drinkers gathering at The Cuckoo's Nest and The Grey Hound and The Armada, formerly The Blue Shark. The Fish was leaving his council house on St John's Terrace, passing the candle factory. Snug in Mother Hubbard's café about a coal fire four phlegmatic Yorkshiremen fell to discussing Nostradamus, that seer of doom. The tide was flooding in past the Bulman Bar where the great O'Leary was downing a dark potion of draught Guinness as daylight faded from the western windows.

It was you and I who walked out of town, the fancy-woman and her rake going by the old ramparts, the site of the Blind Gate, the ground of the old battlefield, not shooting pool in the Dunderrow Bar, you all in grey and the rake in handwoven Donegal tweed jacket, hardly appropriate but purchased in Kildare Street, Dublin, to attend luncheon at Iveagh House upon the invitation of D ˙ FitzGerald, to honour the King and Queen of Spain – handsome Don Carlos and his lovely consort over on their first state visit.

Paddy Locke and Garr dived into The Lobster Pot.

Monsignor Cosimo Bumperini, SJ, was lavishly entertaining Canon Norman Prior at The Blue Haven in Kinsale, pouring Muscadet with a steady and liberal hand.

'A glass of wine, Canon?'

Canon Prior graciously inclined his head.

'*Ecco, two* glasses of new wine. *Et on mange des asperges . . .*'

Canon Prior, a tall grey Anglican, amused his convivial Italian host with an anecdote involving his only son Peregrine who had attended a fancy-dress ball at Acton's Hotel, got up as a dustbin.

'*Basta!*' cried the mellow monsignor, laughing indulgently. '*Audaces fortuna iuvat,* if I recall my Horace correctly.'

'And does not Strabo say – '

'Ah, *Strabo!*'

Their choice of fish was sole for the canon, turbot for the monsignor; their preferred tipple Muscadet, to be followed by sherbet and three-star brandy with the coffee.

Nipping the end off a Dutch corona with a gold clippers taken from a fob pocket Monsignor Bumperini was regaling the canon with a first-hand account of his audience with the pope at the Vatican the previous summer, together with an assembly of bishops from Rome.

A majestic tubular figure vested in shimmering white received them, took his hand in both of His, smiled without condescension, or so it seemed, looking into his eyes as if He could see into his heart. Pope John Paul II, Karol Wojtyła, the former Bishop of Kraków, was an aristocratic figure with a great domed forehead.

From a capacious inside pocket the pope drew out a thick punch of keys but seemed uncertain of which key fitted which lock, indeed seemed unfamiliar with the topography of the Vatican, its labyrinthine ways. He waited smiling before the door of the Pontifical Antechamber. On the other side stood Swiss Guards, tall and upright, barely breathing, still as statues. His Holiness stood smiling, key in hand, not uttering a word in the gorgeous room covered in red damask.

The Vatican doors were invisible once they were closed, no lock or doorknob to be seen, covered in *boiseries*, all sealed mysterious chambers. The smiling Polish Presence was lost, had not been long in office; his composure was absolute, a figure cast in bronze.

Canon Prior was moderately intrigued, sniffing his Hennessy, keeping his thoughts to himself. The monsignor was positively twinkling, now puffing a thumping big King Edward corona.

Staggering from The Lobster Pot, Paddy Locke now full to the gills made his way on foot and alone past the scum on the Scilly dam, smelling (Paddy, not the dam) even more powerfully than before of creosote (an odour similar to smoked meat), damp rope and stale Guinness, stole up the hill by The Spaniard and in with him to The Spinnaker, of all places, where presently in an indistinct rapid manner, like a priest muttering Latin Mass, he recited swiftly the Ballad of the Crossbarry Queer for the benefit of the two foreign nancy-boys got up in fine expensive clothes:

> Now wimmendowimmen
> an' mendomen . . .*

---

* The Ballad of the Crossbarry Queer:

In the town of Crossbarry
Where I was born,
A fine strapping lad,
And they called me John Curran.
    Now women do women
    And men do men;
But best of all was when John did a hen!
And when John passed away and went down to Hell
He did have a go at Satan as well.
Satan stood up and asked 'Whom have we here?'
And John answered back 'It's the Crossbarry Queer!'

The ethnic air has a cruel country twist to it, its intent to belittle and begrudge all strangeness, all non-Irishness; death and dishonour to all deviants.

'*Progettare è un poco sognare . . . ?*' one polite Italian queen questioned the other. 'Do we not detect a certain foul smell?'

'Willy singyouse anudder?'

'I scarcely think so, no thank you.' Does he not see his snot's dripping into his drink? he asked the other in Italian.

Paddy could not help it, snot the colour of *eau de Nil* was depending from each nostril, every now and again hastily snuffled back, like mercury rising and falling in a pipette.

'Hoose rownn?' he asked truculently, wiping snot with the back of his hand. 'Hoosa rownn nowah?'

The two foreign gentlemen finished their whiskey without undue haste, donned mufflers and street-clothes and quietly departed, bidding adieu in dumbshow.

Heaving a heavy sigh Paddy Locke sunk into a stupefied reverie.

Time passed. Others came and went. Paddy slept, standing like a horse at the bar.

Canvas cap askew, Lanky Locke was smoking a roll-up and dribbling, wracked by storms of coughing, his head down, the spent roll-up between his fingers so stained with nicotine they might have been dipped in cowdung.

He heaved and groaned, resting his raging temple on the cool bar counter (as if he had removed his head from a sack), staring down at twin boots the colour of diseased brass, side by side an immense distance below, stapled to the floor.

'Ah no,' groaned Paddy, 'fuck me, no.'

The floor came up at him then sank away again.

'*Buenos tardes, amigo!*' came a loud convivial hail from somewhere in the mist and who was it but Steamboat himself up from the loading dock and coming through now, four sheets to the wind, having had a few in the Fishermen's Wharf Bar. A hard fraternal fist smote Paddy between the shoulderblades and Steamboat's whiskery voice breathed hotly into one ear.

'Get this down you.'

61

Opening one eye Paddy Locke perceived a glass of the *hard stuff* not six inches away from his nose, levitating along the bar counter, where in the far distance the hazy shape of Steamboat was gesticulating, glass in hand.

The cast of Paddy's eye was watery, all mucus and tears, the eyes opaque and out of alignment, muddy as the gaze of a carp or bream.

'Down with her, Paddy.'

Paddy Locke rested his head against the counter and backed away, holding onto an invisible rail, like a bullock in a pen, and made a low rumbling fart in his breeches not dissimilar to distant summer thunder, but mercifully odourless.

'Do youse wanna anudder?'

This time, by Jove, he broke wind almost soundlessly, a summery zephyr surging and soughing through swaying boscage, setting all astir and away in its path and releasing the delicate aromas of pollen and blossom and sap-crammed leaf, though the stench now released into the bar was another matter.

'A wettan windy May fillsda barn with corn an' hay,' said Paddy, upright and teetering, straightening his cap. He was five feet four inches and rarely sober if he could help it, *if* he could afford it. At times he ate a block of ice-cream, the only food he could hold down. He screwed his old soiled canvas cap into alignment with his nose, swivelling it about his overheated skull as if adjusting the lid of a pot.

'Two moons in May means no money an' no tay.'

'The hard Paddy,' said Steamboat.

'I'm fullassa tick,' said Paddy thickly. 'Fuller *nor* a tick. A wet ass an' a hungry gut.'

'The hard Paddy.'

'No, no,' said Paddy darkly, now thoroughly cross-eyed in drink with whiskey raging through him. 'Am drunker nora cunt.'

Paddy Locke convulsed his features and seemed to concentrate himself intensely as he shrank to the size of a low, bandy-legged basset, unearther of foxes and badgers. After some deliberation, with head invisible between his shoulders and both hands gripping the bar counter, he released one concluding mighty obbligato.

On the roadstead the rusty coaster *Paz*, out from the Gold Coast with a cargo of soya pellets for livestock, long in service, long as a street in Valparaíso, was pushing slowly upstream on the flooding tide. At other times and other tides it would be maize or sunflower or rape-seed from Amsterdam and Hamburg, but today on this tide it was soya pellets from the Gold Coast for the tranquillized pigs and heavily injected heifers of Munster with a long wet winter behind them and they in need of protein to ready them for suburban tables throughout the land. Out from Kinsale went malting barley for the Continent, and in came this.

One of the deckhands was walking on his hands along the hold covered in blue tarpaulin stretched tight as a drum. Some others leaned upon the taffrail, smoking, ears pricked for the banshee wail of '*Cabo de velho*', the famous Irish death-cry. A mile ahead the warps were readied, The Fish and Steamboat standing by, spitting on their hands.

The Polish herring fleet was in, a dozen dirty factory ships, some moored out in the bay, others up and down the river as far as the new bridge, one a Soviet spy ship, the stink of fish-guts pervasive, the ravening gulls thick on the tide. No Poles set foot onshore. If any crewman defected the captain would be shot on return to port, where life was hard, a man had to hold down two jobs, for Poland was poor. Work began on the factory ships at seven in the morning, the winches groaning. Rowing boats pulled out after dark for trade in poteen and Polish vodka.

Summercove was to starboard, the slip, the Bulman Bar, a warm fire, the *habitués*, had the frozen observers on the taffrail been free to avail themselves of it, the bar with smoke rising from its chimney.

Ensconced as usual in the left chimneybreast and roasted on one side by the coal fire burning in the grate, Trapper Revatta, lean as a leprechaun, dozed by his half-consumed pint of Guinness and glass of port, as down the chimney floated the voice of his late brother Fred, a murmur hardly distinguishable from the low noise of the fire, whispering confidentially that the hereafter was savage altogether. *Brutal*, said the unseen one.

Not that the sleeping Trapper minded, for he had no belief in an afterlife; life here on earth was enough and more than enough.

Shocken, breathed the disembodied voice down the flue. *This place is pure hell, Joe boy.*

Steam rose from the Trapper's mucky boots. He had been labouring long hours in the freezing Fort Charles.

Tell us, the dead brother whispered in a coaxy voice, *what goes up the chimney down and down the chimney up?* Oft-times the mood was on him for levity, but when in God's name would you find levity in a dump the like of this? The stacked fire made a gentle sibilant sound as if calling to bats and the Trapper, awakened by the voices of spooks, stared wildly about him with eyes that had the whey-blue sheen found inside mussel-shells, the left eye blind. But only O'Leary, enormously elongated, was perched on his stool by the door, immersed in a crossword puzzle.

Breathing thinly the Trapper sipped port the colour of blood which brought back a little life into him. He felt thinly alert again, there by the good fire set by Willie.

A stud, answered the voice in the chimney with low laughter. *A stud in a man's boot.*

The voice came laughing down the chimney. The Trapper dozed off, hands plunged in trouser pockets, his breathing soft as a hare in a mountain form.

When he surfaced again the bar was flooded with an agreeable amber afterlight, an old amber bottle in which the newcomers (a young Australian couple from the youth hostel) moved sluggish as fish in a tinted glass tank. Their voices rose and fell, coming from the antipodes.

'Me head is leppen,' muttered the Trapper, and the gnarled hands wormy with old veins clasped themselves convulsively about his knees.

Willie's ingle was a wobby kind of a place frequented by spooks. Casting a squinty look about him the Trapper reached up with a trembling hand for the pint three-quarters emptied on the low mantel.

'Illin,' Joe murmured coaxingly. 'Givesa nudder pint, Illin. Me head do be leppen.'

Transfixed, Helen Fair was staring out the window. The Trapper hung his head and glared at this hands as if at strange appendages that did not belong to him.

The finest day that ivver came outa de hivens! the whispery disembodied voice breathed down the flue.

'Lave us now,' mumbled Joe, bowed as a pair of calipers, cross, fuming.

A gust of smoke blew back down the chimney.

'He do,' the Trapper said to the smouldering fire in the narrow grate, 'he do.'

Helen Fair began absently polishing a pint glass.

'Illin,' murmured Joe patiently. 'Givesa port here, Illin. Me head do be *leppen*!'

'Oh God my legs are killing me,' sighed Helen Fair.

Pollard pellets and locust beans came in on all the tides for Good's mills, for the rats on the roadside and the hungry birds of the air, for the cattle in the drenched fields. A high-pitched grinding sound from the swivelling crane working on the dock carried on the wind to Summercove and was heard in the Bulman when the door was open, heard by Trapper Revatta in the ingle, the great *auriculae* pricked up and attentive. He knew from what quarter the wind blew, where the tide was, without consulting the papers.

'Are you trying to give me a hard time, Joe?'

'No, no, Illin, no,' the Trapper said, rising awkwardly to his feet, blinking with smeary, blurred, frantic blue eyes.

'Well then, will you behave yourself?'

Trapper Revatta's home was a cosy place down the Bulman lane. Reclusive brother Tom had converted it from a lofty pig-shed into a narrow L-shaped abode similar to a railway carriage, if somewhat damp; and there Joe lived alone, within hailing distance of the brother. There was little communication between them. Brother Tom lived in the main house, not drinking alcohol nor smoking tobacco, disapproving of Joe's wayward ways.

Since his fishing days ended the Trapper had been an employee of the Office of Public Works, and carried with him the foul weather from Fort Charles; for up there on the eminence a cold wind blew winter and summer, from time immemorial. The trapper worked with a long-handled shovel, leaning on it as on a crutch, his mouth ajar, wisps of hair escaping from under his cap. He was sixty-two years old but might have passed for a man much older; his moods varied. He drank pints of draught Guinness with shots of port, a strange mixture. He was his own man.

The great O'Leary was absently trimming and manicuring his broken black fingernails with the edge of a Yale key on a bunch that included penknife and corkscrew with an instrument for removing stones from hooves, sourly observed by Helen Fair who was bored out of her wits, having pulled pints on and off since midday when she came on duty, when not selling sweets to children over the counter. The great O'Leary had mentioned trouble with his passport, stamped UDA by the Israeli authorities, and how he, the undesirable alien, had hopes of employment in Reykjavik, gutting fish, or work in Algeria, or maybe Australia, work of an unspecified but lucrative nature.

A pugnacious bachelor with missing front teeth to prove it, he had been sent packing from a kibbutz, deported from Israel. Taking offence at words let drop he had stuck the prongs of a dining-fork into a man's throat with a quick lunge across the refectory table.

All day long he drank draught Guinness, going through the *Mirror* and *Cork Examiner*, laughing his head off, analysing world news, local scandal, calling for refills. Gossip and hot scandal were his style. The long hours spent in the bar, always on the same high stool or standing by, had become a *Missa pro defunctis* celebrated alone, just as if he were dead to the world and ready for the grave. He had a rough tongue but a good heart. The fuckers had it made, he said, all bets covered. The best possibilities were always out of reach. The fix was in.

His manner was to make a mockery of everything. He had teeth missing, was held by indolence. Looking out now he saw the ghostly vessel passing by and dark faces aft peering across the taffrail where the Panamian flag hung limp.

'Nignogs,' said the great O'Leary, 'floating by.'

The tide continued up the sea wall. The wake of *Paz* slapped against the rocks, ran up the slip. The acrobat on the hold was upright now, hosing down the tarpaulin. From the transistor behind the bar counter the voice of the late John Lennon sang of all the lonely people.

'Oh God am I *bored*,' groaned Helen Fair, yawning, delicate as a cat. 'I need to be kept humoured.'

But the great O'Leary was again lost in a crossword.

The best single of all time, averred the imbecile on Radio 2. 'Of all, *all* time.' Radio Dublin was always blathering away near the serving hatch, in the best of times, the worst of times. The great O'Leary, the Bulman's most reliable customer, lived alone in a caravan parked rent-free in a field owned by Billy O'Brien to windward of a hedge of ash and beech near a gate into the property not one Irish mile from Ballymacus Creek where you swam nude near two swans that had flown in from Oysterhaven Bay.

The great O'Leary owned few personal possessions beyond the clothes on his back, a two-stroke made way for the Suzuki GSX 250, second-hand, before that he had footed it the six miles to and from the Bulman Bar and the uncertain humours of its owner, to the caravan parked to windward of a hedge as if it had come down out of the sky.

Above the field, the rich grass ravelled by the wind, the larks sang in spring, spiralling up into the clouds. Unseen corncrakes *kraak-krakk*ed in summer, the pale Brindley beauty alighted on the hedgerows amid wild garlic. In winter it was a different story. Then the caravan trembled and took a pounding from a freezing south-easterly blowing over Oysterhaven Bay and the flatlands of east Cork. Out at Ballymacus Point the red-haired Daw Harding took ill again.

The undesirable alien was five feet ten inches in height, weighed eight stone six ounces which put him in the welterweight class, was thirty-three years old and could let down pints until the cows came home. The great O'Leary was a deep reader of newspapers, addicted to crosswords in the *Cork Examiner*, the London *Mirror*, Philip Elting's *Herald Tribune*. He read through them all in his free time, of which he seemed to have an inordinate amount. As with the booze and roll-up tobacco, newsprint and press photos of the world's calamities were meat and drink to Tomás, forms of sedation, forgetfulness.

The rich dead Beatle sang of the moribund northern city, the once great port, its factories closed and its docks dead, sang of Eleanor Rigby, of Liverpool, of all the lonely people.

'This kind of weather gives me the pip,' said Helen Fair, cross as a rat.

The great O'Leary said nothing, standing as if turned to stone at the end of the bar, lost to the *Cork Examiner* ('Oxx has the form').

'Mind you . . .' said Helen Fair, but did not pursue the matter further, staring abstracted out the window like Rapunzel locked up in her tower.

'Nice an' gloomy in here,' murmured Joe Revatta to the fire.

The great O'Leary was lost in a Cork fog. The absented right hand felt for the pint, found it, he drank with his eyes still fixed on newsprint ('Bishop's plea sparks walkout'), inhaling Old Holborn roll-ups. He turned a page to the crosword puzzle and Joe Revatta continued to stare into the fire, while Helen Fair gazed out the window.

'*Apiarist!*' suddenly cried out the great O'Leary, briskly shuffling his dirty great combat boots, and marked it down in rude capitals.

An enigmatic (all Munster) caption raged across the opposite page: 'REIGN OF TERROR BY BRUTE DAD.'

A reprise of the opening toccata.

Now, swelling as if it meant business, the tide came flooding in from beyond the Bulman buoy. The fire was dying in the hearth and the last rounds called. It was closing time in the bar and the great O'Leary at last feeling the drag and pull of an immense fatigue mixed with a nameless sadness, having stood a good twelve hours and swallowed fourteen pints, as he had put away sixteen the day before and maybe nineteen the day before that again in a week where all the days had run together to this moment in an endless time of unemployment, during which he had run up a colossal tab with Willie O'Brien, not always the most patient of publicans.

Crouched at the other end of the counter under the old faded sepia photographs now turning up at the edges, the faces of dead fishermen and the great fishes caught, seated at *his* place and grave as an owl in a tod of ivy, under twitching eyebrows his enemy watched, heard the high intemperate speech, the loud guffaws, noted the flushed visage, the sign language for the tab, wished him ill.

But now it was closing time and Willie with his high cries was driving them all out into the night. *Thou shalt not*, his enemy thought, wiping his mouth, moving last. *You O'Leary.*

The tide had finally crept up the sea wall and over the slip where oystercatchers took wing. The gulls were calling out sadly over the river at Summercove where everybody gets up everybody else's nose all the time.

'Night, Dick.'

A bad-sign sickle moon was riding high above Kinsale, dragging the evening star on her back. It would rain tomorrow. And in the air, stronger than ozone or seaweed, the stench of herring guts was stronger than ammonia.

Then one day I'd come upon Paddy Locke lurching about the place with his eyes crooked under the soiled cloth cap a size or two too small for the heated head; with a yaw to the left and then to the right, once even seen teetering up Friary Lane under the fine stand of elms by the grotto to the Virgin, and then swallowed up by the dark open door of the friary, perhaps gone to whisper his sins into the sympathetic ear of a Carmelite friar.

Or again standing on one leg outside The Lobster Pot, The Oyster Inn or The Harp and Shamrock, low in funds and uncertain whether to enter or not. Or doing sentry duty outside the Temperance Hall, or lurching and tacking with some other inshore fishermen by the Scilly dam, come from The Spaniard, squinting at the girls' legs. On those rare occasions he would address me quite civilly as 'Killer'; I never knew why.

Paddy sometimes gave the impression of being a sleep-walker in broad daylight. The cloth cap stuck on casually at an unusual angle or pressed awry on the pointed skull, and from under it the wandering cock-eyed stare askew, and Paddy advancing crabwise in a series of somnambulistic staggers alongside the tidal shifts of the Scilly dam, bound for The Spaniard or tottering by the Temperance Hall and the Methodist church (a total of five active parishioners) and up the lane by Jim Edwards' gorgeous handpainted sign for Restaurant and Bar on a blue ground executed by Paula's da; and so to The Harp and Shamrock or The Glen, where a pint would be started at the pumps the moment Paddy sidled in.

One late December afternoon at close of day we were walking the ring road, heading for drinks at the Bulman, when we saw the Trapper Revatta and a stout co-worker from the Office of Public Works knocking off for the day. The long-handled shovels on their shoulders might have been pikes. They were the very image of the defeated stragglers of 1601 heading home with pikes shouldered, silhouetted against the pale stone of Fort Charles and the steely dying light on the Bandon beyond, around about the 387th anniversary of the defeat, 'defiantly conceding the battle'. Chased over all the fields and ditches of Belgooly and Ballyshannon by Carew's shouting troopers, Wingfield's horse; beshitting their breeches and calling for protection to the Virgin. Two gallant figures on a windswept hill, going home.

Trooper Revatta. His only luxury a warming-stone in the cold bachelor's bed; not the last man in Ireland to try warming his bed with a stone (*cloch*).

An English captain wrote home by rushlight in a damp Godforsaken place: 'Quite a number of our Foe whom I hath Personally Dispatched in the act of scaling walls or retreating but still menacing with Catcalls, Jeers, etcetera not infrequently hath I seen again, still alive and jeering, and *must kill again*. Come to parley or surrender, hurling down abuse and Offensive Matter (faecal) from breached Castle walls.

'That is ever the way with Winter Campaigns, of which this must be the Foremost and engaged in the fowlest Weather. It seems the Enemy is everywhere, lying low to spring at us — a Hydra-headed monster that has to be slaughtered not once but many times. Or else every Irishman hath ten brothers.

'Ye will scarce credit this, but yesterday at a plashy place called Ballymakkus did see a flock of white-breasted birds flying *backwards and upside-down* over a low hill by the Creek, with high cheeping cries as the *picho ichos* in Spain. The Irish have a name for these. They fly fast in flocks and seem to lay their eggs in thickets.'

'They do come in March,' said Billy O'Brien, screwing up his eyes and nodding his head. 'They hatches on the rocks.' He didn't know their name, a name in Irish.

Two fishermen in yellow oilskins were chopping off fish-heads on the deck of the *Sovereign Dawn* moored out on a bobbing orange buoy off Summercove. The men worked methodically, spilling the guts one way, tossing the headless fish into barrels. Seagulls squabbled over the remains as it was carried out by the tide.

The great O'Leary came in by the back door bringing with him a powerful gust of freezing air.

'Begod,' he said amiably, 'it's snowing in the jakes.'

'Yesterday was the holy fly altogether,' the Trapper said. Helen Fair said nothing.

Next morning the river was all grey and nothing moving on it but a motor launch with a party of men in drab suiting — perhaps mourners — setting off to drop ashes, human remains of some citizen departed this life who didn't wish to be buried in St Multose or St Eltin's six feet under, being taken out to the fishing-grounds beyond the Bulman buoy.

The cat's narrow head, a skull covered in fur, with whiskers, pushed into my hand, began purring. The heating system was on but the cat's purring was louder, I could feel it running up my arm. The motor launch had disappeared around the corner. The area once half grass was now all cement, the Bulman car park. The professional gambler who was married to the female professional psychiatrist, a disciple of Jung, drove up from Cork in his beaten-up old Ford to park in the car park by the Bulman slip and gaze for hours at a stretch at his old home, now owned by an American belly-dancer and her computer husband.

Matty Maunsell was just stepping into the Bulman, having removed his swanky pork-pie hat and scratched his head as if his brains were boiling and then replacing the hat and going into the deserted bar. And then came a couple of tourists with backpacks to gaze in stupefaction at the slip, the tidal river, the fort across the way, the Bulman sign, as if these prodigies of nature had just come into existence before their astonished eyes. The sightseers stood bemused in the middle of the road, reading the signs and portents.

Within the Bulman now a neat fire had been set and all the table-tops given a wipe by Willie O'Brien the publican.

'I'd be in the *horrors* of drink!' cried Willie to no one in particular, throwing a fierce challenging look about.

'He was in this morning trying to sell me a *blast* of glasses!' Willie was flitting to and fro on the catwalk behind the counter, checking up, poring over the *Cork Examiner*, keeping always a weather eye on the great O'Leary.

He was a shortish broad man with a somewhat waspish nature, a high intelligent cranium and short-cropped black hair going grey about the ears; hair which on occasion could *stand on end*. He had the threatening stare of a little auk ('high, shrill laughing chatter') and early in October flew out with his nice wife Kay to the Canaries and Portugal, for a change of air.

'He'd try to sell you *anything*!'

The great O'Leary studied the tricky crossword puzzle like a graphologist confronted by a bogus signature.

'I couldn't believe anybody would sink so low!'

Nobody said a word.

'He's too exuberant isn't he?'

Little auks breed on broken rocky cliffs. They have a basilisk glare in the eye sometimes, for life is very hard and unyielding for auks, who are ever anxious, rightly or wrongly feeling themselves to be a threatened species; although Willie O'Brien as a publican did alright for himself. And publicans are by no means a threatened species in County Cork, quite the contrary. All competition was removed a mile away at The Spaniard, or three miles in another direction at fabled Belgooly, a haunt of Provos, fervent if misguided nationalists who had blown up a couple of tracking stations atop Mount Gabriel, mistakenly supposed to be British Army surveillance plants on Munster soil. With bombs, sectarian killing, hunger strikes, protection rackets and their own excrement, the Belgooly boys would free old Ireland once again of the Sassanach yoke.

This little auk was grey about the ears and spoke, in intense and compromising vagaries, between clenched teeth. He was a proper bridge fiend.

The 'nameless' Irish bird had three names in English, on the word of no less an authority than the great Engish ornithologist Sir William Jardine, who called them fallow-smith, whitear, white-tail or white-rump. It can be easily identified by the white rump as it flits from stone to stone, appearing to fall, then resuming its erratic flight. It *appears* white-breasted because it flies backwards and you are looking at its rump, not its chest. The whitear arrives in Ireland in March or April, always alone, flying swiftly over the east coast to her high nesting grounds.

Billy O'Brien of Ballymacus was a dapper (does not Milton refer to 'dapper elves'?) little man with glazy eyes in a wrinkled weatherbeaten face made distinctive by the arched, truculent nose of Punch. He was not related to bossy Willie O'Brien of Ardbrack, bridge-player, setter of fires, good husband of Kay, father of Peter and Patricia, vacationer in the Canaries and Portugal. This arbitrator of arguments would sometimes bar O'Leary or Maunsell from his licensed premises for periods of probation, turn and turn about. Billy O'Brien was the kind landlord of O'Leary who paid no rent. Blinking his eyes and nodding his head, his eyes reduced to mere slits, Billy moved his shoulders inside his jacket like a small disgruntled bird ruffling its feathers.

Billy referred to 'a fierce quiet man in a hat' (in the sense that horses are 'fierce cute', or highly intelligent); meaning the man rarely spoke, never removed his hat. Then the nod, the blink, the fluffing up of feathers, the look of keen perplexity.

Matty Maunsell had worked as a driver and rigger in Fosset's Circus, erecting and taking down the marquee. Once he had 'lost' a lion in Inchicore. He was a great reader of books, pulp literature, a persistent cadger; there was the remnants of a natty dresser. He wore a posh pork-pie hat in order to doff it to the ladies, tilting it, the lid of a kettle on the boil, an archaic and charming gesture. He did not go as far as to hold the pork-pie like a begging bowl, but the gesture had in it something of a begging of charity invoked in silence. Matty was sixty-three years of age, but could have passed for seventy-two; a Protestant, his memory going, or gone.

While Matty's acrylic mottled grey pork-pie suggested old gentility, Paddy Locke's cap had a vaguely seafaring appearance, a longshoreman's headgear. He did not conform to one's notion of fisherman, nor had I ever seen him rowing a boat or letting down a lobster pot or pulling in a net; he looked more like a superannuated boxer, with the bow-legged appearance and battered face of a bantam-weight.

I had seen him unsoberly hang over the river-wall to call out abuse and encouragement to those below on the rocks, at the back-breaking labour of pulling in nets, fishing for salmon in the ebb-tide.

Guard Concannon the opera buff sang a deep bass, had a smattering of Italian and learnt some French from the Basque fishermen, drove an expensive car, the property of his brother-in-law Ned, and 'had it in' for you, over some parking dispute. He was a strict law-enforcement officer of the stamp of 'Bow-Wow', 'Bald Tyres' and the peerless 'Book and Pencil'.

Guard Con Concannon sang like a bull in the choirloft, boomed away in his big bass in *Ruddigore* under The Buck's uplifted baton, tore into *La Traviata*: '*Tra-la-LAA! Thummm. Tum-te-tum-te-TUAM!*' So sang big Con, all lower jaw, taciturnity forgotten, the serious face awash in sweat: a *singing* bull, by God!

74

Willie O'Brien spoke in exclamation marks.

'Whackers' was to be seen tying up his green front door with a length of frayed rope and sallying forth to collect odds and ends of timber for his fire. The fishmonger Murphy looked after him, saw that he did not want. Mackerel were down again, praise be to God: three medium-sized for 75p were laid out on the slab like survivors from the Ark.

Whackers clung to the hand-rail at the foot of Friary Lane under the stand of elms, with jackdaws and cats, addressed a listless lady down from her prayers at the friary, telling her of the destructive habits of the grey crows, prone to pick out the eyes of newborn lambs.

'Is that *so* now?'

Stout young Finn hired two ethnic groups on a pro rata basis and they played in the front Armada bar on alternative weeks, one week the ruddy-cheeked Firebolgs and the next the ranting and roaring Tuath de Denaans. Their music sounded identical.

With the darkness would arrive bodhran player, fiddler, maybe a penny-whistler, a conceited vocalist with stunned female groupie in tow; an excrescence of folkish fancy, promised a fair fee in advance. Stereotypes are never good.

On a high bar stool sat the Farting Farmer with plump right fist clamped to his pint of draught Guinness, perspiring like a pig. The Firebolgs were the right boyos!

The songs came gustily as the west wind blowing over boglands, flattening grass and up-ending swans in tarns the colour of lapis lazuli, whistling through the crannies of a remote cottage perched somewhere in the back of beyond, entering a death-room and pushing aside a curtain to discover an inert corpse laid out, looking down its nose at the bare upturned feet, the waxen hands manacled with rosary beads. The surly brutes were never at a loss when spouting out ripe runic wisdom, frothing a little at the mouth betimes, chaunting with the drone of the war-pipes, glottal stops in the throat, droning away for form's sake. 'The Town I Loved So Well' was from the ever-expanding repertoire of the peerless Furey Brothers, a twosome matchless in their invocation of the Irish *Schicksal* (destiny) whistling down a hollow tube. They played in the long front bar where the atmosphere was presently sauna-like.

This chaunting folk music (diddley-diddley shit) went down very well. Finn told me that there was *mighty history* about the Old Head, the McCarthy lands and castles plundered by the Norman de Courceys.

'That place is rotten with McCarthys. Beyond Summercove they're all either McCarthys or Hurleys.'

The whole place was rotten with history; Summercove itself a haunt of suicides.

Your grandmother was buried in the little cemetery hard by Fort Charles, where you took me on our first walk. The Foleys lay for all eternity with their toes to the tides, your granny with her two children; one had died at eight months and the other not much older, of diphtheria.

In October the little port began to stink of fish; if you were walking down the Cork road, the smell of herring came to meet you. Three Polish factory ships were moored upriver between the Trident Hotel and the new bridge. Trawlers followed the herring shoals around the coast, coming from as far as Killibegs.

At other times the town smelled of brewery; from the malty stock-feed transported from the holds of foreign coasters into Good's mills opposite the Pier Cinema and the dead railway station on Knocknabohinny.

A bearded worker was letting down a plumbline from the ramparts of the French Prison in the rain, the corrugated roof having been removed, as also the slate roof of the friary, pending renovations by the Office of Public and E & T Builders respectively.

A young worker got out of his pick-up truck and pressed the chiming bell of a house called Deas Mumhan near the postbox let into the wall, the red initials VR were now painted green, and someone had cut 'sex' with a penknife. The worker threw pebbles against an upstairs window. Presently there the curtains were drawn a little apart and a hand signalled.

Two little girls were passing below Friary Lane, one blessed herself in mid-leap as they skipped on down the hill past the French Prison where scaffolding had been erected against the window embrasures. The little girls skipped on past Deas Mumhan and its neighbour Mel Teog, where dwelt lace-curtain Irish. 'SEAN O'NEILL, ESTATE AGENT', a sign said sadly.

Miley Murphy was plucking a cock pheasant in the middle of his bicycle shop and two large dogs with tongues lolling were stuck together at Boland's corner.

The tide was almost fully out around the batteries of Fort Charles where half a dozen bored English soldiers had done themselves in at the turn of the century; there as a child you had played around the battlements.

From southern Europe in May, flying over the Brenner, came the red admirals to breed in the nettles.

3
1937
My Parents; the Suicided Corpse

Back into the past, back into the past; and lo and behold, another picture begins to form. On a collapsed sofa before a roaring coal fire two choleric European gentlemen sit side by side, engaged in sporadic guttural conversation. One is grossly corpulent, with protruding froggy eyes, who wheezes like a Pekinese. His companion is tall and dark-visaged with a smoky complexion. With the delicacy of lemurs they pick chocolate biscuits off the paper doily on the plate.

Our drawing-room is permeated with an unfamiliar and disturbing foreign odour; strong ship's tobacco fumes drift and through this smokescreen boom two unearthly voices. They seem to be noisily engaged in clearing their vocal passages of phlegm; but in sober truth they are speaking in Flemish. *Walloons!*

The larynx dark and stained: an infernal machine or sounding-box, brutal, emitting unknown sounds and never-before-heard inflexions, intonations signifying God knows what – gorilla talk. The Bogey Man mutters from an unknown and terrible ambience. That was how men communicated on the Continent, with this dark talk; enough to give you the shivers. And women, how did they talk – quacking like ducks? The females quacking, their Calibans grunting; a lingo of long ago.

The fat one is called Fatty Geldorf, and the tall dark one is my uncle Juss Moorkens, the go-between when my parents began courting in Longford.

'Barty will follow on bicycle!'

In one gloved hand my father, Bartholomew Joseph Higgins, holds the reins; with his free hand he withdraws a large service revolver from an inside pocket. The moon comes out from behind clouds and artfully illuminates the long dangerous barrel, the oiled chambers. My mother straightens her corseted back and her eyes sparkle, as my progenitor cocks the Browning.

'Did you ever see,' he waggishly asks her, 'ever in your life see such a large revolver, Lilian Boyd?'

No indeed, she never had.

Brandishing the Browning and with whip aloft my ardent progenitor drives the high-stepping mare at a spanking pace down the Battery Road in Longford town, pursued by all the local dogs. He is deep in one of those daydreams that can overtake even the shallowest of men; it is like being in the midst of the most tumultuous of parties. My mother is aglow, luminous with happiness. English troops are garrisoned in Longford barracks. My father-to-be is protecting my mother-to-be from the murderous Black and Tans who travel about Ireland in Crossley tenders, intent upon murdering innocent Irish.

Another picture is thrown on the magic-lantern screen, or double bedsheet, by an anxious and shaky hand. Silently and with jerky movements, a line of ashen-faced men in baggy uniforms, with packs on their backs, rise up from a trench and cheering wildly stumble forward into the German gas-attack. Poison fumes drift over no man's land. My uncle Juss prepares go to into action with the Belgian troops. He carries part of a machine-gun. On his feet, army boots, puttees. On his face a dreadful expression. On his head a pot-shaped helmet with a ridged backbone down the crown. I seem to hear the weak cries of the attack foundering in the gas.

Now Juss stands with arms folded across his chest and legs planted wide on the duckboard in the trench, smoking his pipe, helmetless, his dark sad eyes stare directly out at me. In the sepia background are trees with their heads blown off, shell craters filled with water, tangles of barbed wire in a torn-up and blasted wasteland: Flanders Fields. This the Box Brownie has captured for the heavy family album and for perpetuity: '*Uncle Juss gone to war*'.

The Belgian army was almost totally wiped out in the first

assault in 1914 and took little part in the action except in a very confined and quiet sector at the edge of the Western Front. Juss was well under age when he joined up. After the war he returned to Longford to live with two aunts, and became a renowned dry-fly fisher; in time he opened a shop selling angling equipment in Dublin.

But I see now a man's long figure with its head in a gas oven (from his mouth he had always seemed to exhale dangerous fumes), the body covered with the greatcoat, his head in the oven, breathing in gas. Speculations about a living person only begin to be legitimate when the ascertainable has been ascertained as far as possible. My mother had some intuition of his end – suicide in Dublin – but never told his wife, soon to be widowed, my auntie Evelyn, who was her younger sister.

You told me your nightmare of a windowless room and a frozen corpse stretched out on the slab. The naked Juss had committed suicide and seemed to be sweating. That was your prophetic nightmare.

Two years later Uncle Juss's eldest son Gustave was brought by Civic Guards into the Dublin morgue to identify his dead father. When he stepped into the windowless room to be confronted by the naked and sweating corpse on the slab he had entered my mother's nightmare. There was the windowless room; the long naked man on the freezing slab was his dead suicide father; my mother's dream was out.

I open the heavy family album and on a station platform somewhere in Belgium soldiers stare at me; behind them across the carriages ' *HOMMES ET CHEVAUX* ' is painted. I enter another nightmare. My mother understands French; she tells me what the words mean: men and horses. I look into this sepia photo: the staring soldiers on the Belgian platform, the train being loaded up for war, and the word that presently will come to mind is *abattoir*.

My mother sits on the window-seat, calmly knitting, pulling out wool from a bag looped about the wrist. She counts the stitches, a wide mesh made with big wooden knitting-needles, as the summer rain pelts down outside. Hazy cattle drift across Mangan's field beyond the plantation, over the road. The distant Dublin hills have disappeared, the Hell Fire Club now vanished from the summit, veiled by fretting rain.

'Gallant little Belgium,' sighs my mother, but she is more likely thinking: 'Poor Juss!'

Summer rain strikes at an angle to make tea-coloured puddles on the recently scuffled gravel before the house, indenting and pitting it with little Vs that go running across like shivers. I thought then: Strange, strange . . . I'll understand this when I'm older.

I am older; and I don't understand.

My father wanted none of us to leave home, ever. Possibly he was not such a common type after all. At all events he did not care to reveal himself to me in whom my embittered mother, who had married him for his money, had buried very deeply her disappointments. His access to us, his four sons, was cut off by her in a calculated smear campaign ('That bloody fool!'). So he drifted away. They drifted apart, as is the way of marriage. Their graves in Dean's Grange cemetery are not adjacent.

The Tiger Moth flew low over Springfield, the goggled pilot (known to my father) waved gallantly before cutting through the telegraph wires that ran from the roof into a great beech tree in the meadow and from there to the mains on the road beyond the plantation. The flimsy wings wobbled, the engine coughed, struts flew loose.

'By Christ he's down!' cried my father, delighted. But he made it over the trees, heading for Baldonnel. When the Emergency came, Heinkels and Dorniers flew over, off course; Lysanders of the Irish Air Force (motto: 'Small But Fierce') took off in the opposite direction, hid in the clouds. The Luftwaffe, playing their *Schlagermusik*, dropped sticks of bombs on the North Strand in Dublin. The earth-tremor from the high explosives ran twelve miles underground and all the pheasants in Killadoon Wood screamed together, as our windows rattled and woke me.

Carnation petals lie like drops of blood on the uneven paving-stones of the glasshouse that smells of ferns and tomatoes, of summer heat. Beyond the smudged glass my mother weeds in the rockery, wearing gardening gloves and an old broken hat, smoking Gold Flake to keep the midges away. She cuts flowers for the high altar at Straffen church. Long-stemmed delphiniums stand in a bucket of water. She has one bloodshot eye, knows the names of all the flowers, even the smallest rock flowers, and speaks of their health and welfare as if they were human. She says gardening calms her nerves, suffers from claustrophobia and cannot go to Mass, cannot be in a crowd ('bad for the nerves'). My father, hands in pockets, strolls in the walled rockery. They seem a pair, yet apart.

In a field near the Hill of Ardrass the last triangle of wheat is being cut by the reaper-and-binder. The last rabbits hop away before the guns. A limp dead line of them are laid out on sacks. The dogs sniff at their bloodstained noses and back away, licking their chops and looking shifty. The reaper-and-binder raises its steel teeth and sets them into the wheat.

On an old tandem bike hired out for the day my brother and I cycle on through Taghadoe, Dowdstown, Monacoole, Castle Dillon, Priorstown, Tibberstown, Pluckstown, Celbridge, Newbridge, Lady Chapel, Hazelhatch and Raheen in County Kildare. It is one life.

It is a day.

Frère Jacques,
Bruder Jacques

1984

To the memory of
Bartholomew ('Batty') Joseph Higgins
1891–1969

Yes, suddenly I saw it all, the mists cleared and there it was before me. Inspiration means starting a new story. Or so say the Zen Gaels. To begin something is to leave off something else. Begin again. Do not look back.

Oh he was a young one once, and very thin. With so much changed, it hardly seems my life today. Unnatural child, unnatural son, sickly adolescent, mistrustful young man, unnatural lover, unnatural husband, unnatural father, as grandfather-to-be.

I went in mortal fear of my own dear Da. *Vater*, *Padre*, that small bully with the mind of a lathe-turner; a sad cliché. I feared him, his waspish humours, his orders, until I'd made him a grandfather, turned the tables, cut him down to size. He passed away in a suburban Dublin nursing home fifteen years ago when we were in Berlin. It was May then, as now. We flew out from Dublin on a lovely blue day. It was a perfect day for flying, you said.

I recall two incidents, insignificant in themselves: as the single-decker bus pulled away from Killiney village the word 'NO' appeared in white paint, hoved into view on the wall opposite the Sylvan Café. On the towpath by Dun Laoghaire station our small middle son, closing his eyes and opening his mouth like a pup, deposited two pukes. We were away.

My mother had died two years previously, of a brain haemorrhage. My father was dying of cancer. They had cut him up. It did no good; he was going anyway. I believe he had grown tired of life, as the guest who goes out for cigarettes and forgets to come back. Reality was receding from him, or he from reality; it amounts to the same thing.

85

The blood halted in the veins, the face turned to the wall, *Misserfolg*, senses thickening, leaving the physical behind, the marrowbones freezing. Then a sudden blaze of darkness into the dying face. Then it was all over. Or so I imagined it. By then we were in the *Landhaus* at Dahlem; settling in.

My mother had despised him. She rarely spoke well of her Batty. Perhaps she hated him? When she had departed in the night, taking her hard feelings with her, he had to follow. There was no other way.

He was the only son in a family of fifteen – was it? – horse-faced sisters, my aunts; which may have explained his furtiveness and evasiveness, fear of exposure; not exactly rowdy nor calm, not assured, but something hidden in between, a little craven. Fidgety, uxorious, a stater of platitudes, an anti-Semite, a great scuffler of gravel, a copious tea-imbiber, a starer-out-of-windows, a great gossip, poking into his earhole with a safety match. His toilet was extravagant: the brown suit, the fawn outfit with hacking-jacket; he took hours preparing for town – a regular pasha.

Kildare is a place of follies.

Satan was reputed to have dined at Castletown House, following phenomenal participation at a hunt. He was invited to dinner, and cards after; he dropped the ace of spades. Stooping, the maid saw the cloven feet. He disappeared up the chimney in a puff of smoke; the priest sweated seven shirts and died.

I knew *my* place – a thin-shanked Papist child, permanently unwell, difficult to feed, fearful of everything, of most people. Priests and civic guards particularly; hidden behind the old cook's skirt, or in the shrubbery, or behind the kitchen mangle where the cats made their stinks. Or in the back-yard cowshed, with the cowshit, or in the plantation in the stench of suppuration.

I conceived myself to be permanently guilty, though of what I could not say ('unclean thoughts') and suffered the agonies of the damned before Confession, the weekly ordeal-in-the-dark, whispering sweet nothings into a priest's inclined ear, behind the grille. With nuns and priests

I lost my nerve altogether, became even more furtive. They were unreal, scarcely human.

'He's getting red again! . . . LOOK, he's got the guilty look!' I had the guilty look and could do nothing about it.

For my father, the hardest thing to believe in, to credit, was his own existence, a very Irish trait. He frittered money away when he had it; it didn't interest him. This stranger to honest toil had never worked a day in his life. For most of it he had lived on inherited money, a copper mine in Arizona; and when it was gone he lived on credit, loans. And when that was gone, on hope of winning the Irish Sweep, even the Malta Sweep. He lived on hope, long odds.

In summers he hid himself away in the long uncut grass of the orchard, braced himself for the Irish sun, covered like a wrestler in cod-liver oil. The long winters 'took it out of him': what winter could not remove was laziness, nothing could shift that.

We, his four shy sons, hid in trees or perched on garden walls, observing him. To all callers he was not at home. We were instructed to say that he was 'out', or 'not well', or (a last resort) 'gone away'. He wanted to add, 'for good', but feared to go too far. Foxy in his slyness he waited, hid. He invented a stubborn ailment; the old appendix was at him again. 'It has me crippled.'

We bore no malice towards him but we feared him, for he had bullying ways. To those he knew to be his social superiors he was all affability, brazening it out – the merest bravado. He shrank as he aged. Finally he became pathetic. He wanted to be left alone. He was my Da.

The notion of paying taxes was repugnant to him. He owned three gate-lodges. One stood empty, condemned by the Health Authority. One poor consumptive needy tenant paid no rent for years, passing away in Peamount Sanatorium.

Major Brookes hid in a bush on his own driveway when the tax inspector called, as he did once in five years. My father hid himself in the orchard, ferocious in appearance as a Pawnee on the warpath. He was the narrow fellow in the grass, Pawnee or Cree brave with thoughts of scalps on his mind, breathing deeply, the deep breathing of the Plains Indian. Or an Aztec roasting himself in the sun. Or the fearless fire-eater of Mexico City on Avenida Reforma, a waterway when Montezuma rode out in his feathers, anticipating stout Hernán Cortés, but dreading his arrival. He is eating the fire. Behind it all intense fear. This was my mulberry-coloured father scorched royal purple, the sun-worshipper who got so little of what he loved.

My three brothers and I, taciturn, well-spaced-out walkers, none on speaking terms, arrived at Hazelhatch Station with what my father termed 'a good two hours' to wait, following an early rise, ablutions, best clothes, a two-mile walk. My father and the station-master, a Mr Darlington, paced up and down the departure platform, stopping every now and then for my father to emphasize a point; the lugubrious man narrowly observed my father, nodded, sucked Zubes. They recommended pacing and my brothers and I watched them in sullen silence.

A slow bemused sick goldfish rotated slowly in a tank of unchanged greenish water at the top of the stairs at number 11 Springhill Park, Killiney, a private nursing home for the dying. A stale spent smell permeated the place. The old were sunken into easy-chairs in an overheated room, their eyes fixed unsteadily on wavering images on the television screen. They were looked after by a brisk ruddy-faced ex-nurse, the Presbyterian Mrs Hill. She and my father had disliked each other on sight. He referred to her as 'the Presbyterian bitch', snuffling up his nose, ruffling his feathers.

The old man's unsteady mind was elsewhere now, going into senility, approaching that terminus called Final Insolvency; his muddled thoughts fitfully dwelling on the past, pushed about like drifting clouds. Not much strength was left in him, tilted forward from his bedroom chair, hands out to the glow of the single electric bar. His fingers clenched and re-clenched, an old tomcat feeling the fires.

His liquids had been 'cut down'. In the WC he knelt, flushed the toilet, drank from cupped hands.

Frère Jacques, Bruder Jacques

The dying moved about in a daze, the stairs creaked, a door closed. The old ones assembled in the living-room downstairs, read outdated magazines through quizzing glasses, dozed on their chairs, waiting for the next meal. Mrs Hill was rigorously cheerful.

My old man sat forward at a dangerous angle from the chintz-covered chair, sunken into a past that no longer belonged to him. Ireland was finished, he said. And so was he. The Presbyterian bitch watched his every move. She spoke to my brother and I at the foot of the stairs. Had any *arrangements* been made? She did not expect this patient to last much longer; one could not expect miracles.

My father examined the contents of his pocket, abulge with letters, newspaper clippings, a stub for the Malta Sweep. Dr Duff the kidney expert was in sporadic attendance. It was May with all the gardens in bloom.

Dr Duff, in passing, tapped the glass tank of unclean water and the sick goldfish turned slowly over, giddily dying.

Perhaps he was not a kidney expert but a cancer expert? But are there cancer experts? He descended the stairs, smiling.

We stayed over in Killiney near The Druids' Chair public house, put up by a couple called Harper. Mr Harper had red hair and was Irish. Young Mrs Harper was English. She wore hotpants, stood on a table to clean a window, walked alone near the monument. A donkey grazed in a field below with a jackdaw on its back. A lawnmower was being pushed back and forth, back and forth through thick scrub grass. A mist rolled in from the bay, covering all in a trice. With much squealing of brakes the number 59 red single-decker bus went into a tight turn by the Sylvan Café, past the stern injunction 'NO'. A white fog of freezing air curled past the closed windows of Regan's airless lounge where a Mayoman with incipient jigs raised a double brandy to his lips. Out of the fog came a pony and trap carrying tinkers with their pots and pans, with redheaded children clinging on. This nomadic entourage out of the past swept by, the little fast-trotting donkey goaded on with stick and curses. the father stood, clutching the reins, flogging him; the lot vanishing into the whiteness, down the hill.

I walked across the park to Killiney Hill, looked down into the seaweed beds. In a grim snug in Dalkey village a betting man encircled Royal Braide in the list of afternoon runners at Leopardstown. My father held a hot toddy between his hands and stared at me with unsteady watery blue eyes.

'This isn't right, Aidan. I never thought I'd come to this.'

He moves inchmeal; the surgery has been too extreme. I feel my fingertips tingle. I beg a lift down the hill in a passing car. We end up in Fitzgerald's.

A white mist rolled in from the bay, covering Dalkey Island. In the clinging whiteness a lone blackbird sings sweetly. Above the low door of the sunken Gents a notice reads: 'MIND YOUR HEAD'. My fingers still tingle. The face in the mirror tells me: One day you too will be old and helpless.

My father was drifting in his thoughts that wandered around in vaguely concentric circles, where choice seemed both endless and tiresomely circumscribed. That was the way out.

Near the bottom of the tank a sick goldfish was suspended upside down with its intestines hanging out.

May 27th, 1969 was a bright sunny day, all blue sky, a perfect day for flying. We flew from Dublin Airport to Heathrow, stood among rude Germans for the Lufthansa flight via Bremen and Hanover to Tempelhof, Berlin. The Germans wore curious hats, pressed to the front of the queue.

A little time passed.

We were living in a rented mansion in Nikolassee, near Schlachtensee and Krumme Lanke. French divers were crawling around the bed of the Oxo-brown lake in search of parts of a Lancaster bomber shot down in the *Kriegsjahre*. On a raft a diver set out wet darkened fragments. No bones. A woodpecker drilled into a tree above the path. The American army drilled away in the woods near the border – a mailed fist knocking on a heavy door that will not open.

Sinister grey battle-tanks rolled along the grand *Allees*, their pointed gun-barrels inscribed with the names of Berlin sectors: Dalhem Friedenau, Schöneberg, Charlottenburg. In the postbox by number 52 Beskidenstrasse a brief postcard from my brother: *Father died yesterday. Sunday.* Dated 29.6.69.

Muss es sein: es muss sein. The earth pulls towards it all living things.

The Gnostics believed that the angels put to every dead person the same question: Where do you come from?

I bought a bottle of Jameson, his preferred tipple, accepted change from mildewed fingers. *Danke, danke, mein Herr!* Yesterday there was three days past here. My father would be buried already in Dean's Grange cemetery.

I walked through the Joachim-Klepper-Weg, broke off a sprig of flowering shrub. The stately house was lit up like a liner going through a dark sea. I poured out three libations, for the Aztec, the Red Indian, the dead Irishman.

My three small sons were having agreeable hysterics in a hot bath upstairs. You were singing '*Frère Jacques*' to them, in German. They were laughing their little heads off. Tracery of leaves, tracery of leaves. They looked so defenceless in the deep Berliner bath, wet as seals, laughing at the absurdity of the '*Bruder Jacques*', their Germanic antics.

That which we are must cease to be, that we may come to pass in the being of another. Exist anew! A page was turned, an old man sighed. Leaves fell from the linden tree. A link, a link!

Helsingør Station

1972

1
Matterly Light

In Denmark every day is different; so say the old books. It's made up of islands, every island different, and a witch on each. There are over three hundred of them. I knew one of them once. She lived in Copenhagen, that port up there on Kattegat. We were fire and water, like Kafka and Milena, a daring combination only for people who believe in transformations, or like boiling water. You were Mathilda de la Mole.

No, you were you to the end of your days. Why should I complain? The other day I was thinking of you.

The pale Swedish dramatist who lives over on Sortedam Dossering with a distinguished Danish theatrical lady claims that he has learnt Danish in bed. Across the long wall of the Kommune Hospital a solicitous female hand had inscribed a proclamation to the effect that many of the nurses there are lesbian, too. Ten years ago the nurses of this city were regarded as being no better than common whores.

Down there in a basement you had lived like a rat with good old Psycho, in a lice-ridden hole below street level in a kind of cellar, the walls green with mould. Water dripped from above, you suffered, Petrusjka was but a babe. The place was full of furnace fumes by day, rats ran about at night, chewed up your stockings. Drunks fell down into the area. You lived there then. I didn't know you. Where was I?

This Danish capital is a tidy well-run place. The little grey city is relatively free of the subversive aerosol squirt and graffiti-smeared walls of West Berlin; though the pedestrian underpass near Bar Lustig is marked with a daring axiom to

95

the effect that *Kusse er godt for hodet* or cunt is good for the head, with a crude heart pierced by an arrow.

You wrapped newspapers inside your clothes, crouched behind Psycho Kaare, your arms about him, bound for Sweden. That was your life then. All the associations with your lovers seem to have been pre-ordained, moving rapidly towards consummation. He was the third man in your life. Blind in one eye, 192 centimetres tall, a failed dramatist turned carpenter, transvestite, father-to-be of little Petrusjka Kaare.

You lied to the shop-girls. The outsize dresses were not for 'a big mum', but for Psycho, wanting the impossible, garbed in female attire, ill, unshaven, chain-smoking, drinking Luksus beer, looking out the window into the street of whores. There was a strange smell off his breath. Both of you were undernourished, half starving. You left him, lived with an alcoholic pianist for three weeks. Then you couldn't stand it any more – there was an even worse smell off *him*. Empty turps bottles crowded the W C. You swallowed your pride and approached your mother for a loan. Mrs Edith Olsen gave it grudgingly. You returned to Psycho, the tall unshaven figure in the chair, dressed as a woman, looking out the window.

Then you were standing for an endless time with your hand on the red Polish kettle that was getting warmer and warmer; knowing that an important moment had arrived for you. You would go to bed with him. He would be the father of your only child. So nothing is ever entirely wasted, nothing ever entirely spent. Something always remains. What? Shall I tell you?

Oh he was a young man once, and very thin. He knew Sweden, had been there before. He arranged the papers for renting a house. It was cheap there then. He was writing one-act plays, a mixture of Dada and Monty Python. They were funny. He sat cross-legged on a chair, typing away, laughing. As a child he had done homework with frozen feet stuck to the cold floor. The Royal Theatre rejected the plays. You loved him. Light came from his face. He was young once; not any more. In his early forties he had begun to grow old. Now he is a dead man.

The motorbike, covered in sacks, hid under snow. All the boards in the hut creaked. Winter pressed down on the roof. In the *dacha*, you and Psycho began starving again. A plump partridge strutted up and down in the garden every evening. Each evening it returned. Armed with a stick Psycho waited behind a tree. You watched from the window. The bird was too clever, Psycho too weak with hunger, the cooking-pot stayed empty. You wept.

Then Psycho couldn't stand it any longer and left for Copenhagen, the cellar and the rats. He couldn't take it any longer. You couldn't bear to return and stayed on. You were alone for weeks, made a fire at night, to keep off the living men, and the dead men too. The dead were full of guile and slippery as eels.

Going into Sweden on the back of Psycho's motorbike you had almost died of cold. Motorcyclists are known to experience a sense of detachment, and *may not even recall arriving at their destination*. St Brendan the Navigator saw Judas chained to an iceberg in the middle of the Atlantic. It happened once a year, by God's mercy, a day's relief for the betrayer from his prison in the everlasting fires of Hell.

But you accepted all the buffetings of fate. You walked into the forest. You said: 'It's difficult to think in a forest. I am thinking *av karse*, but the thought never finds its end, as near the mountains or by the sea. It's heavy in there, the wall of trees keeps out the sun. There is absolute silence in a Swedish forest, no singing birds there. Even the *uuuls* are silent. Oh that was a miss for me.'

In the forest you came face to face with an elk. The great prehistoric head was suddenly there, the mighty span of horns, the mossy tines, set like an ancient plough into the weighty head. You glared, separated by only the breadth of a bedroom. The great beast was grey all over, like a certain type of small Spanish wild flower found in the hills. The dead flower in the jar of the Cómpeta bedroom.

Then, without a sound, without breaking a twig, the elk faded away into the forest. It was very quiet there. Heavy too, like the Swedes themselves. They worked all day, raced home in identical Volvos in the evening, closed their doors.

It was a *Shakespearean* forest, you thought, with no dead leaves, no undergrowth, but mossy underfoot. The light there was very dim, angled in, then draining away. *Matterly light*, you thought. Elks moved always in 'matterly light', fading back into the silence out of which they had come. The Swedish-Shakespearean wilderness.

Perhaps the best idea is to imagine a country, never going there. Otherwise you end up writing impressionistic letters from abroad, while feeling superior to those who stayed at home.

We were in Spain, in a *pueblo* in the sierras. It was raining. Outside, a narrow wet street of glistening umbrellas. We sat in a window annexe, waited an hour for a poor meal. You didn't mind, drinking *vino*, telling me about your flat, where I had never been. You described it. The Russian icon with the bullet-hole. It had been torn from a Moscow wall during the Revolution. You described the delicate colours of a Chinese scroll. The pewter candlestick of 1840 with a lump of lead soldered into it, making it less valuable. Your apartment overlooked the lake. Your landlady was unhinged. From a ground-floor window she watched you come and go, wanted to get you out. You rode a tall old bike. Psycho worked as a self-employed carpenter above the brothel quarter.

'I always talk in showers,' you said, 'and then I am sad.' Your green eyes, as if never seeing clearly what they looked at, looked at me, took me in. Who was this? You seemed to be chewing on memories of other times, places, situations, other loves. You travelled about, to Venice, the Scilly Isles, Greece, finally Spain, where I was to meet you. At Naxos you saw the sea-bed of the most delicate character, and 'there the finest sands I have ever seen'. In Tripoli, of all places, you found timelessness. You felt at home there in its endless evenings, far from the Western mess.

Pastel was your favourite shade. The long evenings on Naxos, where you had mourned a lost love, were pastel-coloured. Not mauve, not lilac, nor scarlet as on the Algarve. You, Misery's Mistress, grown beautiful, in sunglasses, walked through pastel shades. The 'Greekish' men chased scantily-clad foreign women into the sea or through the pine woods. Hippies copulated in the most public places. On the beach, in the backs of crowded buses.

You told me of your first love. It wasn't really love. His name had been Olsen too, a married man. You went to bed with him in Olsen's Hotel because he had spoken lovingly to you of his wife, then in childbed. You were on a cycling trip with your plain friend Alice. You were sixteen, become attractive after endless puberty. It was Easter 1958 at Holbæk, sixty kilometers from Copenhagen. Hymns were relayed from a loudspeaker into the square. You ordered Tuborg, an orange juice for Alice. You wore jeans and an anorak, a late developer, flat-chested. You entered the men's toilet by mistake after the Tuborg and came out whistling to hide your embarrassment. 'I thought it were a boy,' remarked a rustic.

Bjørn Olsen was a commercial traveller in perfumes. He was kind. At first you said no and then yes. You were shocked by the size of his prick. This was serious stuff. But it wasn't love.

You were nineteen in the country, the plainness of puberty gone. You spent a weekend with a couple of friends and ended up in bed with them. Andersen the painter was 'insatiable and fucked all the good-looking girls'. He wanted you in bed with his beautiful redheaded wife. First her and then you. Andersen would not take no. The whole house creaked.

You tried to take your life by opening a vein in your wrist with the point of a pencil. It had nothing to do with Andersen, you didn't want to live, had nothing to live for, you opened the vein, closed your eyes, covering yourself with your overcoat.

'But, as you see, I recovered. Afterwards you feel worse than before. I felt so ashamed. You are still alive and the bed soaked with blood.'

Things will never be the same again. No, things are the same as they always were, only you're the same too, so things will never be the same again. I say things but I may mean times and places. Times with you. Is the memory of things better than the things themselves? We will never know. But no matter what happens I still love you very much, though obviously in my life 'love' has to be betrayed, and many times. I do not know why this is so. I only know I am relieved to have finished, yet in a perverse way I'm still the same, and nothing has changed.

In a stand of oak a leaf falls. Queen Caroline Mathilde, dressed as a man, goes out riding. She is on the lookout for the son of the German cobbler Struensee with whom she is besotted. He enjoys her favours, in between advising the king – and who is himself insane and knows full well that the queen's condition is incurable.

We stayed in a hotel in Málaga, coming and going like marine creatures in a grotto of transparent water, in the depths of the fine old mirrors set into the doors of two hanging cupboards in room *numero* 37 on the fourth floor of Hotel Residencia Cataluña on Plaza del Obispo facing the cathedral. The gonging bell galvanized us at every stroke. At the corner some stonemasons were chipping away tirelessly at tombstones, covered in fine white dust.

You told me of Diana's mirrors, Nero's sunken brothel-ships. We went out. You found it was cold and returned for your poncho. The lift-attendant asked were you married. I bought a small hand-mirror for Petrusjka, whom I had never seen. I told you about the red spot on Jupiter. When daylight struck the bevelled edges, the mirrors threw out rainbow hues. We came and went in them, nude as newts, as in a deep-focus medium shot thrown on the black-and-white screen by Toland. They were fine old-fashioned mirrors such as you do not come across today. Whatever has happened to those far-off happy days? Were they happy days? Was being with you happiness for me? And with me for you? Were we happy then?

One morning you said it was beginning to end, you could feel it. You had to go away again. The return flight was booked. The stonemasons continued chipping away covered in fine dust, as we went past for the last time. Málaga was Yo-Yo mad. It was the day of the *Subnormales*. A

child dressed up as a bride was being photographed in the
Alameda Gardens as we passed through, climbing up though
the levels of the Alcazaba, past the cruising gays anxious as
whippets. Below appeared the bullring, the sanded oval,
tiers of empty seats; beyond it the port. A long rusty Soviet
oil-tanker lay to in the dazzling bay. Covered in sweat we
climbed to the Hotel Gibralfaro, which belongs to another
European time. Maids in black taffeta were waiting at table. I
was charged 400 pesetas for a half bottle of chilled
Valdepeñas. Over by the bar stood von Stroheim, the great
director of *Greed*, with his back to us, in riding-breeches,
whip under one arm, a monocle screwed into one eye-
socket, throwing back double Scotch. We returned to our
room late.

A seal-like hooded statue of Rasmussen in stone stands on
the Strandvej promenade, a memorial to the hero of Thule.
We walked hand in hand down the promenade, which was
the length of your own childhood. To our left the seal-like
hooded figure stared out towards Kattegat. An ever-alert eye
peered out under bushy eyebrows stiff with hoarfrost. We
took a number 1 bus to Central Station, and walked out from
here. You said you wanted to show me places from your
past. We presently found one and went in. It was full of
Danes. A pianist crouched over the keyboard and sang like a
woman, high and mocking. Then a burly friend from the
past came in, embraced you. He sat at the piano, began to
play. It was part of the past when you had lived like a rat with
good old Psycho. Someone had tried to cook their semen in a
frying-pan. Perhaps the pianist?

Danish was very much a language of the stomach, you
told me. *'Mave'* had a 'stomach-sound', as Mogens Glistrup
was a most Danish name, Danish as Trudholm. 'Everything
is dangerous to a Dane.' By Thulevej a signpost above a small
cliff, more chine than cliff, warns wanderers of *livsfare
jordskred*, unsteady earth.

Your apartment did not disappoint. It was the sort of nest
you would find to live in, irregular in shape, with windows
overlooking the lake. Your abode. I was there with you. The

last swallows flew over the yacht basin and a skiff with two active oarsmen went skimming by. It was a bright September Sunday. Light scudded off the water, the clouds drifted high up.

You had read Walter Schubart's *Religion og Erotik* in translation and were full of it, spoke slightingly of St Paul, convert and martyr. He whom you called Paulus of Tarsus had 'fucked up' the teachings of Christ and changed Christendom.

And then? The wind threshing the hedges at Melby. A blue crossing over Kattegat (for we were *en route* for Rørvig) Six passengers sat silently in the narrow cabin as we crossed a thoroughly Danish sea to Skanse Hage. In the *fiskhus* the flounders caught that morning at Isefjord were breathing their last.

In the *bodega* at Hundested, that Place of Dogs, the recorded voice of Kathleen Ferrier sang 'Jesu, Joy of Man's Desiring' on the muted transistor. You had sung this at the top of your voice as a child, standing on a chair, to the astonishment of Papa Olsen, who played a cornet from the back of a truck with his group on Labour Day. In the yard an outsize dog frisked about our table. From another table an unsober Dane asked you: 'Why don't you come over and sit with us, and tell that fellow to go back to wherever he came from?'

And now we are approaching the Rasmussenhus. The signs have become vague and weathered; we are nearing the homestead of the hero of Thule. The dormer window overlook Kattegat. He had built the house with his own hands. Before entering these hallowed precincts I enter you near the cliff-face in the long grass, removing the minimum of clothes. We hear Danish voices passing amicably through the hidden paths.

He died in hospital outside Copenhagen in 1934, when was seven years old and you not yet born. He died of flu an eating rotten seal-meat. He was fifty-four. His rare wind swept spirit abides at Thulevej, in the Rasmussenhus so back among fir trees, protected from the elements. It look out always at Kattegat's tides, sails, gulls, swans, the air an

)eace. His kayak hangs from a beam. His hunting-spears are
here. A great pot-bellied stove occupies the study where he
vrote up his diary, where a large white cat followed us
ilently from room to room.

LEV LESBISK' is painted prominently athwart the bridge
ipproaches at Peblingessen. For fine young women live
iusbandless today in Denmark, with single children secure
n carriers, cycling home from Klampenborg. The young
iothers are turning their backs on menfolk, or marriage.
'enus (Lesbia) rules hereabouts.

In the little red train that takes us to Hundested from
iillerød, a woman no longer young is immersed in her book.
'he deliberating eyes are fixed steadfastly on the text, her
low right hand turns another page, as we move through this
rdered countryside. A lynx-faced cat mews miserably in a
asket. A drunk raises a Hof beer on a passing platform. The
ead of the cat is pushed out of sight by an abstracted female
and. Single dogs go prowling in the fields so bare of
vestock or any living thing. Even birdlife is missing. The
'heat stubble is burning, scarring the fields with long black
nes. The windbreaks are odd-looking things, if they are
'indbreaks. What else could they be?

Last spring we passed Kokkedal's cut hayfields. The dry
ay was lying in neat swathes. Mown wheat. Cyclists drifted
'ongside the train, waving, thoroughly Danish, as the train
aversed a region of lilac woods.

Now Vedbæk, Rungstedlund where Baroness Blixen lies
uried under her favourite tree; the Danish poets give
unday readings there. We sat at a table under a tree at
umlebæk, coffee and Cognac before us, looked across at
ie white Swedish shore: a nuclear plant.

2
Thobin Thimm

It is an early September day in Copenhagen, sunny afte
yesterday's rain. Over Øster Søgade the mews make thei
cries of secateurs cutting. It's seventeen feet deep in th
middle and thus cannot be man-made, says the Swedis
dramatist. Trust a Swede to notice that.

Handsome jogging couples pass in jogging outfits. Draine
with fever I sleep. You nurse me. Plain yoghurt, purpl
grapes, chilled Rioja. For review comes *Wise Blood*. Sandr
Holm arrives late and covers the bed in flowers. She is a littl
bull. I have some kind of virus. My temperature is 'midwa
between normal and where you die', the nurse tells m
studying the thermometer. I spend three days in bed.

Then, after washing off the death-sweat, I sally fort
feeling frail, unshaven. Into the thin sunlight, the *Kondilove*
go by, one attached to a dog on a lead. Muddy carp-like fis
hang comatose in the shallow brown waters by the foo
paths. The bomb-shelters are overgrown. In the middle
the lake a small islet is covered in vegetation. In the garden
Bar Lystig a boy sells us grapes. It is autumn now i
Denmark, the air cold and bracing. The foliage hangs stiffly
feel unwell. Cyclists drift by. A crab-red sun sinks over t
pseudo-bridge, a causeway for ingoing and outgoing traffi
The sky is clear as yesterday. Music drifts over the wate
Though unwell, I feel irrationally happy, *feverishly* so. Gree
neon from the Finansbanken spills into Øster Søgade lak
Ambulance sirens sound off incessantly between the tw
hospitals. Danish dead are being hustled in and out.

Four white dray-horses pull a Carlsberg wagon over t
'bridge', out of the past. A municipal cleaner in orange Da

104

Glo sweeps the path. The rush of air from fast cars – angelic wings. I start into a second American title: *Everything That Rises Must Converge*. Feeble things. My fever returns.

It has all come back: coughing, lemon drinks, bed-sweats, dry throat. The nude nurse is in bed with the feverish patient clasped in her arms. An enlarged harvest moon sinks over the pseudo-bridge. Traffic-lights wink and blink like mooring-lights lost in the trees. Tiny Bodini has no peace because of the magnitude of his task. You told me that your grandmother's name had been Lemm, which signifies Prick. She was Pomeranian, made good soups. So you had Hungarian-Pomeranian blood coursing in your veins.

You sat on the sofa, crossed your long stylish legs, stared at me. No one could have guessed what was in that grey-green look, even I did not know. You dialled a number, listened, replaced the receiver. Your transistor played low. Now you are stalking about before the long mirror, dressed only in Italian shoes with five-inch stiletto heels. You are *'paying the world a gleaming lie'*.

Italians applaud at the end of every movement, I tell you. Danes slow-clap to show their appreciation. If the English do it it means the opposite, censure. The Chinese are fond of noise and find silence oppressive. Similarly Greeks and Spaniards. Not so the Danes, you say, rolling your hips at me.

Then, lo and behold, I am well again. An old flame arrives from Jutland. Thobin Thimm is a painter, he and his sister run a rose farm in Jutland. He invites us to dine with him at a new Italian place. Shape of the frog in the sauce. Grapy flavour of Italian wine, tang of the cheese. Petrusjka sits with us, a lady.

I stood you a haircut at Frisør Kirsten's near the Gyldne And or Golden Duck. Kirsten herself cut our hair; she dressed in black leather trousers, her hips bulged seductively as she snipped away with small scissors, and your slanted eyes watched me in the mirror. Thimm had gone to bed with Kirsten Arboll. She had lived in Johannesburg, thought that the blacks had not much to complain about. The sun shone through the glass annexe of the Gyldne And where we drank gin. A numbing wind from Østersøen was sweeping the streets clean. Lutheran bells rang grudgingly in their belfries.

Dyrehaven was a woody place where few people went, with mole-casts between the trees and in the open, where there were low mounds. Baroness Blixen used to walk there. 'A life of sniffing and sleeping and fear,' you said, of the moles. 'What sort of existence was that?' Thobin had departed to Jutland.

Then, one evening, the 'handsome painter chap' Thimm appeared again. He had loved you once, perhaps loved you still. I was just stepping up out of the Chinese take-away when he emerged out of the snow-mist. His overcoat worn as a cloak, arms outstretched after the manner of Count Dracula, his breath steaming. The three of us went to a candlelit bar below street level and drank double Jameson.

One night we (you and I) drank in the *bodega* opposite the Gyldne And until four in the morning and were presented with an almost Swedish bill. You downfaced the rude barman. Your eyes flashed; the cheeky fellow muttered something indistinct; you called out something devastating. The barman wiped his hands on a dirty apron tied about his waist.

There sat Old Fröde the mythical one, a sad man searching for some security and not finding it. You spoke to him.

On the way home I addressed a quiet man who sat on a doorstep with a bottle of beer by him, staring out at the lake. He answered by addressing you in Danish. What had he said? Why not tell your friend to go home.

The days were freezing now. The city prepared for winter. We bought fresh vegetables in the market and fish at the fishmongers, going down a few steps off the street. If a certain window was open in a certain square it meant that an elderly male friend was at home. But the window always remained closed.

Young rollerballers on roller-skates, dressed in combat fatigues and leg-warmers, shot through Jorcks Passage.

That time, that place, was it all your own invention, that you shared with me? And I too perhaps was your invention, and the goings-on in that oddly-shaped apartment, the patent-!eather black court shoes, the Greek–English dictionary – *Zina Skarum 20 Lektioner* – a bowl of Greek pebbles, a narrow bottle containing stones from the Naxos foreshore, a book on Crete (*Kreta: Tegninger og Madstage*), a vase of white tulips, strangely shaped Israeli oranges. The muted telephone whispering, the mews flying over Øster Søgade, the icy air outside, the grey lake. Petrolio was thirty kroner for ten litres, and a Northern winter coming on, Fimbal and Old Fröde went limping through the snow.

You ordered up a double mattress, trade-name Sultan, and argued hotly with the manufacturers over delivery. Then one freezing morning the pantechnicon appeared below, the driver calling up for help. It took three of us to get Sultan into place.

Another morning and another fellow arrived with a bottle of some herbal concoction, good for the digestion. Witch-piss you said it was. The stove went cold again for the second time in one week. We drank the witch-piss under duvet covers, listening to the gull-squall and mew-cry outside. The stove was out, the nights bitterly cold. Every day was different. One Saturday, *Politiken* published a poem of yours that began '*Erotisk . . . lethed*', with a photograph of you in a Phrygian wool cap, looking sultry.

Clouds drifted through the September sky as we walked again through Dyrehaven to the hermitage on the hill. The unwalled, unguarded mansion amid a copse of beech was where the widows of dead Danish kings lived out their retirement. No moat or castle keep separated it from citizens who passed on foot, or horse-riders and pony-trekkers.

A stag was bellowing to its herd of wives near Tre Pile Stedet, or The Three Twigs, where a dumpy sweet-faced woman served you coffee and me red wine, calling out for 'Matthew' in an accent that you swore was Bornholm. We sat at a table outside. There you had come as a child with your parents. There you had sat as a child, heard the warning-bell at the level-crossing, saw the little red train rush through. Heard the hoarse stag-bellow at rutting time, felt the air move. There you were young once, an innocent.

In the flower-shop run by your stepfather-in-law, a

retired sea-captain now working as a pimp for male prosti-
tutes, you told a long witty story in Danish, and the pimp
shook all over, wiping his eyes.

Copenhagen is a city of uneasy old people, who stay
indoors, live on cat-food and dog-food, rarely venture out,
hesitating at street corners, fearful of the wild young, the
nudist park, the drug scene. The young are not much in
evidence except by night in Central Station, bumming
kroner for more beer, collapsing across loaded tables.

City of phantoms, of tired faces, of sailors on shore-leave.
Or German students returning from a trip around the
harbour. The Master Race, you said, were still after the little
Danish butter-hole. Granite port of *Belge brote, somner platte,
frikadeller*. Sing-song musical voices.

The sleepy Danes are modest in a reserved way; reserve
with them being a form of arrogance. Public displays of
anger only amuse them. The music in the bars is muted. In
the San Miguel Bar the flamenco music was turned down.
There is not too much laughter or high spirits in evidence.
These drably dressed citizens of the north are warmly
bundled into their lives. Babes with chronically disgruntled
old faces peer critically from hooded prams. Headscarves are
favoured by the young mothers who move about on high
antiquated bikes. The long *alléer* open like yawns.

Elderly couples walk soberly in lime-green *Loden*s through
the King's Gardens. The males wear pork-pie hats and puff
cigars, the tubby wives go sedately in warm little hats with
feathers, and a dog on a lead as like as not. The feeling is of
sedate bourgeois Germans in a German provincial town, but
don't tell that to a Dane.

Flagstaffs are a feature of the island of Rørvig. Narrow
Danish house-flags get entangled in the firs. The cellar under
your far-sighted father's floorboards yielded up good
home-made schnapps made from herbs, very potent. We
dismantled two single beds and spread mattresses on the
floor. And then went cycling on high old bikes – pedal
backwards to stop – from Helleveg, the way to the sea. A
three-masted schooner appeared out of the haze, and a swan

flew overhead, sawing the air creakily, as I took you in the dunes, in the cold, still feverish.

One day I went by train on my own to Kronborg, to see the castle where Hamlet had 'run around after the ghost of his father'. There is nothing much to see at Elsinore. Shakespeare had heard about it from his friend John Dowland. A Swedish passenger-craft big as a street seemed to be dragging the houses down along the harbour. Minute passengers crossed over by a glassed-in overpass to Helsingør Station.

An ashen-faced invalid in a belted raincoat, moving with pain on two arm-crutches, his mouth set in a grim line, closed the window. So much for fresh air. Now all the windows were sealed tight, an Airedale stinking, no air all the way to Østerport!

I had some words of German, some words of Spanish, but of Danish nothing but '*Skaak!*' and felt a right Charley in the shops where no English was spoken, going out in the cold morning, skinned alive at the corner by the North Sea wind, leaving you and little Petrusjka together on Sultan under the duvet, two pairs of brown eyes watching me from the warmth, I descending steps into the bakery, tore a ticket from the dispenser, waited for my number to be called. But what did '17' sound like in Danish?

Your language sounds more far-off than it is, its pronunciation being far removed from any known thing, to my ears at least. Your misnomers were charming: 'artist's cocks' (artichokes); 'corny cobs' (corncobs); 'upflung waters' (fountains); 'downburnt buildings' (blitzed London); 'ox' (braised beef); 'outsplashed ladies' (the nude models of Delacroix, with their 'fleshful thighs').

'I am uproared,' you said, meaning miffed. 'Moistful,' you said. 'I'd jump into bed with Olaf Palme.' You left *postillons d'amour* lying around. 'Sweetheart – gone for a little walk. The lunch is set for tomorrow instead of today. Kisses – home again soon. Nanna.'

'I look into the mirror sometimes and don't believe what I see' (watching yourself narrowly in the glass). 'I think it's funny to pay the world a gleaming lie' (applying make-up but no lipstick, no scent, no earrings; the scentless perfume was 'Ancient Moose'). Much will have more.

Do you know why witches fly?

You prepared the 'squints' (squids) Bilbao-style in their own ink, following the instructions. Pull the heads off the squids from the bodies and remove and discard the spines and all the internal organs except the ink sacs, which must be put into a cup and reserved. Cut off the testicles just below the eyes and discard the heads. Wash thoroughly. *Calamares en su tinta a la bilbaína.*

Conkers split on the cobbles under the chestnut trees near the yacht basin where the 'damned' Little Mermaid poses so coyly naked on her bronze seat on a boulder there, and a plain girl in a loose-fitting blue T-shirt displays big wobbly breasts as she goes laughing by with her pretty friend, and a company of Danish soldiers in sharp uniforms, with long hair and rifles at the port position, go marching by the Lutheran church where your model friend Sweet Anna was wedded to Strong Sven, the translator of Marquez. It was snowing then. Mr Fimbal the Danish god of hard winters stumbled by with his single arm.

We passed again by a group of stone women all stark naked in stone, tending one who appeared to be injured or in the toils of childbirth.

'What is this?' I asked.

'The Jewish Memorial.'

Professor Tribini, top-hatted and villainously mustachioed, sporting a red carnation in his buttonhole, flashed his gallant ringmaster's eyes at you, all fire and sexual push, at Peter Liep's in Beaulieu, where the railway tracks lead back to Centrum.

Bakken had come before the Tivoli Gardens, you told me. Here was the real rough stuff – sailors on the spree, big strong girls wrestling stark naked in mud. It was slightly before your time.

You had been at a Gyldendal party there, had trouble opening a sealed pat of butter, your dinner partner did it for you. You took him home with you on condition that you rode his tall new bicycle. With skirt rolled about your hips and 'brown all over' and at your most attractive after Naxos, you took him home. It was a time I would never know. You rode slowly home, his hand on the small of your back, through the pre-dawn at Bakken, down the long avenue of trees where we had walked, watched by Professor Tribini, abusing himself behind an oak.

'Oh, I am over-lewd!'

'I was somewhat exalterated,' you said.

You served up an excellent Hungarian soup with sour cream and told me your radio story of Satan in the wood, based on a real lecher, my successor after the time in Spain. You sat opposite me, giving me the eye. You'd certainly been at the Cognac again, a couple of snorters before setting out.

We were in Spain again. You had been going on about 'Paulus of Tarsus'. We were in an olive-grove below the logging trail and heard the damnedest noise rising up out of the valley, a strange inconstant murmurous belling, bleating and baaing.

Some time later, over a drink at Viento de Palmas, a herd of over a thousand shorn sheep and lambs went tripping past, with active dogs as outriders and rough-looking shepherds bringing up the rear. The din was stirring – bells, barking, baaing. The shepherds did not stop for drinks, heading on for new pastures.

Now freezing air leaks into the kitchen and you turn the gas low, open the oven door, light candles. The water in the lavatory bowl becomes agitated, as if we were at sea. Sudden gusts of winter air strike through the interstices of the cramped toilet and the floor seems to shift underfoot. The Danes were all secret sailors, you said.

The spiritual suffering of the Swedes (which knows no bounds) is said to be unmatched in any other European country, their suicide rate the highest in the world. By the end of the first quarter of the next century all Sweden would be in the custody of a few large companies, the sameness of Swedish life then complete.

We passed the Jewish Memorial again, the naked women bound together in lumpish humanitarianism. And once your dotty landlady Mrs Andersen passed us on her witch's black bike, sending a hostile look our way.

I write down the magic names:

ØSTERPORT	ØSTER SØGADE	ORDRUP
HUMLEBÆK	HELLERUP	HUNDESTED
KLAMPENBORG	KOKKEDAL	KASTRUP
KRONBORG	SKODSBORG	VEDBÆK
BEAULIEU	RØRVIG	BAKKEN
NIVÅ	ESPERGÆRDE	RUNGSTEDLUND
DYREHAVEN	HELSINGØR	MELBY

In Denmark every day is different; so the old books say. Blow out the light.

The Other Day I Was
Thinking of You

1986

I. Nullgrab

The other day I was thinking of you. Or, rather, of Nullgrab, that quartered city you love so much. It amounts to the same thing. When I recall Berlin I remember you, or vice versa.

Is it even possible to think of somebody in the past? One replaces another in what you call *Herz* and the light goes out. Your voice again; your eyes in the shadows, in the Augustiner Keller under the railway arches at Bahnhof Zoo in the snow, in the Italian restaurant Rusticano with the friendly waiter, in the Yugoslav Hotel Bubec on Mexikoplatz, in the Greek place.

Today is your birthday; a Gemini like John F. Kennedy. The Nullgrab children call '*Nullgrab, det Datum wess ick nich, ick jlob et heesst vergiss nich.*' French kids go: '*Je te tiens, tu me tiens par la barbichette. Le premier de nous deux qui rira, aura une tapette.*' Your expressions were charming. You said 'the Hollands', 'trouts', 'copulations', 'intercourses'. You said: 'What do you think I am – an animal in a box?' 'Yus,' you said, 'yus.' Oh, *quatsch!*

Doch-doch.

Do you recall the Isar flowing strangely in the wrong direction, an invisible deer crashing through the under-growth in the English Garden, the goose-shit around the pond, the tattered tribes of hippies with their guitars below the Minopterus, clustered about the hill? I felt giddy under a tree, the sky whirled above us, it was the beer, the wine, the Cognac of the night before in Schwabing. It was the air, the

115

Föhn, the Bavarian day, the clouds. The trees danced, the earth moved, the air was a-tremble in a manner well calculated to bring on nausea. I lay on my back on a public bench but it was no good, the earth kept moving, the clouds passing overhead; the vegetation danced above my head. You said 'Oh, quatsch!' and took my head onto your lap, laid your cool hand on my heated brow. The earth and the sky stopped their whirling, the giddiness went. Your hand cool, the warmth of your thigh on my neck. Leopoldstrasse was dug up; they were preparing an underground Metro system for the Olympic Games, the killings to come. Our pillow-book was a German translation of *In Watermelon Sugar* which you gave me back into English at a table outside a restaurant in Schwabing, or in bed in the big airy flat in Jakob-Klar-Strasse. On the balcony opposite the retired boxer sat all day, was handed out mugs of beer by his good *Frau*. Your brief silences meant you were reconverting the words of Brautigan into English. You bought a minute bikini in the colour of *café au lait*. For me, it was always a giddy time with you, dearest Schmutz. Perambulating in bright sunlight and the air with an earthy smell, seventeen degrees centigrade in a very lush Bavarian spring.

You suggested a siesta; in German you said it was the little-shepherd-hour. You drew the long semi-transparent drapes, cool air blew in, we removed our clothes. The caterpillar's function is to gorge itself and grow. Linking we walked into the Tiergarten, walked hand in hand over spongy turf. It seemed relatively deserted. I offered to take you in the bushes. Excited Yugoslav *Gastarbeiter* with their shirts off were engaged in an untidy game of *Fussball*. The long column of the golden *Friedensengel* rose up into a clear (Bavarian-blue) Prussian sky. 'Yus,' you said, 'yus.'

The Ominous *Litfassäule*

Beauty is a projection of ugliness – I must have read it somewhere; the notion sounds vaguely French. By developing certain monstrosities we obtain the purest ornaments,

rgued Monsier Jean Genet with characteristically perverse
llipses. Certain dwellings, even certain ruins, and perhaps
hey most of all, reveal and betray the real Nullgrab.

The blackened ruins of the gutted and bullet-riddled
oviet Embassy had been left standing in a nondescript
treet not far from her parents' apartment. Lore showed it to
ie as if unwillingly; something that had to be seen but not
omething that one could be proud of, like her politics. An
igrained dread of Communism that she had inherited from
apa Schröder had induced her to vote for the Christian
emocratic Party. Unsound politics; beware of German
oliticians who come from Bavaria, such as the wild man
trauss. Lore was very conscientious in casting her vote.

You were a child in a city selected for destruction. In a way
iat no other city could be, it belonged to the dead, the burnt-
ut capital of a country devastated. They were everywhere,
id not only in the civil cemeteries between Mariendorf and
ritz; Russian and German dead were overwhelmingly
resent. 'Let's move on,' you said. It was something shameful
ou showed me once. As, at another time, I had opened my fist
id shown you the unspent cartridge I had found in
idergrowth by the water near the Jagdschloss. Something I
ice showed to you. 'Throw it away,' you said.

Always you showed me the Nullgrab ruins with this odd
ffidence, as if proud and ashamed at the same time. The
uttered Italian and Spanish embassies facing the
ergarten, haunt of nocturnal whores. I thought of the liar
alaparte, Count Augustin de Foxa and Count Ciano. Go
uietly, the ghosts are listening. Their embassies were empty
ow as beehives when the bees had gone, a wasps' nest
hen the wasps had been destroyed. They faced into the
ergarten, side by side, dire presences long abandoned but
ot quite dead. A curious atmosphere surrounded them;
ntres of finished ambitions, as Stonehenge and Tara, the
hambra in Granada or the great necropolis at El Alamein.
ieir absolute stillness was perhaps a shocked silence, as if
e hectic life could begin again any day, that gross
lendour and nationalistic fervour renew itself as
onstrously as before.

117

In a tree-lined side-street stood a *Litfassäule*, one of those essentially Nullgraber constructions as truly German a Parisian *pissoirs* are French. The real Axis soul had flown from the abandoned embassies and settled here. On it defaced surfaces a patina of print weathered by time and destroyed back into the acid; for no hand had removed the ordinances, propaganda become threatening even against its own people, and rotted back into a decayed repose - sinister as the anti-tank gun emplacement hidden in a turn of the road by the Rehweise sunken meadows.

I am reading Heine again, about the lovely nixies all dressed in green. Today, stricken with longing, I was thinking of you.

II. Playa de Burriana

For three days the *terral* blew, throwing dust about and making the palms dance. On Playa de Burriana the wind surfers hung about on shore, the Nerja Ski School did little business, damp *Fräuleins* in minute bikinis swarmed in the surf. Back in the hot sand off the shore thoughtful bearded sunbathers adopted lofty Buddhist lotus poses, head resting on palm of open hand, watching the topless parade go by. A form of supplication.

A beautiful face and port from another time – ancient Egypt – her black hair turbaned in a white towel, maroon togs with plunging backline cut to the cleft with a generous play of gluteus muscle, walks with a girlfriend by the Sapphic shoreline; the face hierarchic, remote. Two gays are skimming flat stones while other interested parties watch from behind boulders with bated breath and a stout English man in shorts with very tanned legs practises niblick shots with practice golf balls, chewing on a cigar.

For emphasis, with the English, the voice is lowered modified to the consistent bleat of the tamed middle class expressive of the all-in-oneness of their privileged status. With the Spaniards the voice is raised for emphasis becoming louder lower down the social scale. Headsets are

becoming fashionable among the young, for instant pop
music all day long, the apparatus clamped to both ears like a
hearing-device for the stone deaf, or electrodes for the
brain-damaged.

A Spanish family in high excitement are erecting a
Moorish-style tent in moss-green and raspberry vertical
stripes with dark blue bands and an awning, bang in the
midst of sunbathers. The paraphernalia that people take to
the beach with them! Collapsible camp chairs, mats, inflat-
ble cushions, hampers, beer coolers, beach umbrellas,
transistors, toys for the kids, silent grandmothers.

A parade of the halt and the lame go by, figures from
Breughel or Bosch. It is the day Real Madrid go down to
Liverpool in the European Cup Final. Flies dance in the
ammonia-and-piss reek of the beach privies. In La Barca
merendero the waiters take orders at the double, darting
about in blue singlets and white shorts, barefooted. Piercing
blasts from the cook's whistle disturbs the canary swinging
in its cage and a hermaphrodite assistant grins through the
hatch. A hairy-chested chef whips up cream in a thermos
shaken vigorously near his ear as though preparing a
cocktail. The missing Lord Lucan strolls through.

'Gude bhay ma luve, gude bhay!' a bull voice roars from
an echoing place, apparently from barrel. The canary is
silent now, head sunken in its wing; piercing blasts come
from the galley, the waiters dart about like Keystone Cops. A
tractor harrows the sand where the surf has dampened it,
and a saddleless horse is being ridden into the sea.

Playa de Carabeo is a small horseshoe-shaped beach difficult
to reach, the path down befouled by dogs and children
between the wild begonia beds. The fishermen use the beach
below as dormitory and open latrine, as fishermen have
done since the time of the Redeemer and His Apostles. But
then again it was always a dogs' paradise.

Heavy-beamed peroxided *Fraus* block the entrance of the
librería in the Square of Martyrs behind the church of
Nuestra Señora de las Angustias, Our Lady of Sorrows, hard
by the bordello, fingering *Bunte* and *Stern*, German news-

papers, and an upstart Spaniard drives past the Banco
Andalucía in a new Cortina with an abstracted air. A
sombre *Herr* with a *Mensur* scar is deeply immersed in
Frankfurter Allgemeine Zeitung at a table outside the Ba
Alhambra on the *paseo*, pays with a 5,000 peseta note. José
the waiter in platform heels flips open his change wallet
accepts a small tip. He takes his *señora* for vacation into
Portugal, Lisboa.

III. Rijeka Harbour

An awkward squad of Yugoslav soldiers in baggy pants an
ill-fitting tunics lines up on the quayside near steps that g
down into the still blue water of the harbour towards whicl
a launch with some visiting dignitary aboard is moving, it
flag fluttering in the breeze that blows across the harbour. A
salute is fired and a small figure on the launch offers a bris
salute.

Then the launch draws in alongside the steps and a stou
little man in a linen suit darts nimbly up the steps, where th
stiff squad of awkward soldiers comes to attention as th
white smoke of the gun-salute drifts over the water. It is six
thirty in the morning and the August sun already hot in th
port of Rijeka on the Adriatic Sea, in the long-ago and fai
away, when I went there with you on the way to Cavta
Mlini, Dubrovnik.

IV. Thick Clouds Cover the Sky

Thick clouds cover the sky, then suddenly there is a rift an
we see a wretched little paddleboat pitching off the Iris
coast somewhere towards the end of the nineteent
century. On the exposed deck a young woman, seated. Sh
wears a tweed ulster and poke bonnet and is gazing sadly ou
over the sea. Her husband sits close to her. A singular pale
visaged man in a brown moleskin greatcoat, one hand thru
Bonapart-wise into the breast. The sea wind bends back th

120

brim of a brown felt hat held in place by a length of string which depends from the hatband, secured to a button on the greatcoat. He looks foreign, with his full disgruntled face, the troubled introspective eyes, the bleak regard; he looks ill.

Both are pale-faced, with suffering goitrous eyes; hers cast upward as if in supplication to a Greater Power, more in despair than hope; his probing the space between. Both sit bolt upright as if horrorstruck; just awakening from the conjugal dream. Plunged in deepest despair but united for the nonce in suffering, they stare out over the flying waters at the receding cliffs of England.

V. Turf Boat

The Scalp, Ballylee, Cruachmaa, thistles in a ditch, wind in Belharbour, in Gort, a handsaw sawing in Inchy Wood, water pouring over a low weir, crows over a copse of trees in Kinvarra, a ghost walking in broad daylight in Ballinmantane Castle. Esker, the Burren hills, a lad in a red ganzy, geese crossing the road at Shagwalla, the briny Atlantic crawling in over Bundoran strand. The days full, the tyres hard, the saddle tight, the going grand. Don't let Connemara down! They wouldn't tell you a lie!

A turf boat is lying to with patched brown sails furled. And always the river – murmuring to the right, murmuring to the left, flowing under a humpbacked bridge – Lebane, Roxborough, a hare on the road.

VI. *Kies*: the Passage of Time

The stone returned. Walk again on Burriana beach in the spring. On the sand there with my first-born Carlos. We collect stones, draw figures with a Bic pen.

Flies crawl over the boulders, the waters pour as if they'd always existed, as if I didn't exist. Other eyes, another spirit regard this evidence. Or again: small ants crawl over the rocks. The spirit troubled, conscience troubled. Tumbling

121

water. Troubled water. Wheeling gulls. The riddled sandstone cliff. The high blue sky overhead.

Your guiding hand, your protecting love. Not to hear those three voices call my name again. There is perhaps no seductive alternative worth this loss.

Or again: call me by my pet name again (a guard against loss, like primitive music). For two days, Sunday and following windy *lunes*, both of you were savages with clubs, prehistoric men making obeisance to the tethered mule startled by these formal reverences, bowing down before him. Those three ghosts lately departed for Truss City. A batch of letters abandoned in a drawer. Your guiding hand. Your protecting love. The stone drawn on and returned.

The early departure in the dark, the two buses seen from the terrace, emptiness of feeling. Dozed for an hour and then walked to Fábrica de la Luz, by the ruin, '*Al campamento 10 minutos*', the skull-and-crossbones, '*Peligro ruinas*', the pool abandoned, Elwin's stone named with an extraordinary name.

What came out of the sea was no less than a horror: the owl's orange eyes aflame, a pointed beak, sodden plumage, underfeathers – an old man's skinny shanks in sagging drawers. Oh *búho real*, you eagle-owl, hissing at the Alsatian that kept its distance, what took you into the Mediterranean sea in a morning in May?

My middle son aged ten asked me: 'How can Elijah ascend to Heaven in his bodily shape?'

VII. Autumn Acorns

The autumn of acorns in Highgate Wood and Queens Wood where the mass graves for the Plague dead were dug; archaeologists unearth pottery made by Roman slaves. An autumn of conkers and red berries and an oldish man saying to his wheezing, waddling old dog: 'You're only a big overgrown puppy, that's all you are.'

On the sports field, the cricket pitch surrounded by the wood, the Royal College of Music CC *v.* Belsize Park CC

Two magpies tormenting a hawk in Kenwood, mole-casts in the depression, orange and red berries in profusion. Sign of the end of the world?

Bailey the billygoat, not a normal goat by any means, but rather a sergeant-at-arms goat or company mascot at some military dress occasion, gallops through the wood.

What would winter be without the golden yellow flowers of *Jasminum nudiflorum*? Even the greyest coldest days don't dishearten this beauty for long. In Piccadilly Underground a lovely leggy girl squats before the call-boxes, her head down, eyes closed, curious coloured puke at her feet. All gape at lovely legs, thighs. A still for *I Am a Nymphomaniac* by the sodden steps leading to above ground. The lovely girl vomiting by a dark man, her friend. Xmas spirit in London town.

Mahonia japonica is closely related to lily of the valley, scented flowers that last for months. Put your japonica in a tub at the foot of steps. Lemon yellow flowers on cold foggy evenings, there it is. Foliage for twelve months of the year, flowering for two or three months in winter, tolerant of lime and acid soils, penchant for shade. The lime-tolerant ones prefer shady forecourts. Sarcocolla, Mahonias, skimmias on a north-facing wall, contrasting leaf-forms to delight the beholder. Poinsettias in winter in flower-shops of Notting Hill Gate and Holland Park. Red as red, a Christmas Box.

The Bird I Fancied

1985/1989

Exhausted by the cry that can never end, my love ends; without that cry it were not love but desire, desire does not end.

W. B. Yeats, 'A Vision'

The heart is secret even when the moment it dreamed of has come; if love does a secret thing always, it is to reach backward to a time that could not be known.

Eudora Welty, 'No Place for You, My Love'

1
In the Summer of Imran Khan

He was alone at the end of the bar, staring out of the window above my head, with a pint of Harry's indifferent bitter a third depleted before him, his thoughts miles away. A dead ringer for William Trevor. There were just the two of us in the small bar half an hour after opening time, and Harry eating an apple, minding his own business.

'Excuse me,' said I.

Odd ale-coloured eyes stared at me in astonishment and the gingery hair stood on end.

'You are not William Trevor?'

A slow hand reached out for the dying pint and in a low but distinctly Irish voice he said no he wasn't but not offering to say who he was.

'Pardon the intrusion.'

He did not answer. Vaguely vinegary Irish. This happened in The Coach and Hound, down from Jack Straw's Castle, patronized by queers and queer-bashers, not to be confused with The Coach and Horses, a Young's house near Hampstead tube station, patronized by the fancy.

I had taken to walking from Muswell Hill Broadway by Queen's Wood, Highgate Wood, Ken Wood and across the heath to Harry's quiet bar, which had neither television nor radio, and was run in a quiet and proper fashion by Harry and his sister, Meg.

Jack Trevor Story the thrice-bankrupt one was sometimes to be seen there, firing down double brandies in the company of adoring young floozies. An ex-vaudeville dancer, now well on in years, stood at the horseshoe-shaped bar, gossiping with Harry. The White Russian Lenski, a landscape painter in oils, and his inseparable Estonian friend Malik, refugees from a pogrom, introduced an exotic foreign note to that corner of the bar, to the right as you enter. Jack Trevor Story preferred to sit at the counter with his floozies around him. He had a deep brandy voice.

When old Megs was tippling at the sherry you could wait half an hour to be served. It was a nice quiet bar. The brother and sister drove to the opera in Harry's vintage Overland. The sign of the window read

DNUOH DNA HCAOC

Lamb and Coleridge must have passed by in the old days, deep in conversation, *en route* to the heath, Lamb's dog in tow. (Or was it Leigh Hunt's dog that Lamb was minding while Hunt was languishing in prison for lampooning the Regent?)

A month or two later, with a pint of Directors' set before me, whom did I see but the same Gingery Man once again materializing at the end of the bar, empty at that time; squinting askance into the *Times* crossword. I sidled near.

'You are William Trevor?'

He snorted a short barking laugh and across his freckled features there spread an expression that can only be described as damned shifty. Seen close to he looked a different man.

'Indeed to goodness I am not,' he answered mildly. 'I seem to remember that you asked me that once before.'

Nonplussed I did not reply. It was just after opening time at The Coach and Hound. The Gingery Man looked narrowly at me. His manner was such that did not invite familiarity.

'You don't happen to have been at C— yourself?' he asked, naming the very dump.

Now I was flabbergasted. Amused ale-coloured eyes studied me over the rim of his pint.

'Recognized you at once from a photo in the school mag,' he volunteered in a fruity voice fairly exuding privilege.

I said nothing. He looked uneasily at me as though he had made a social gaffe.

'No offence meant, I'm sure.'
'You evidently are not he,' I said.
'No. Unfortunately not. You know him?'
'No.'

He drew a deep breath and his strange eyes bulged out of their sockets. Then, with a nod, he resumed his intense deliberations with the *Times* crossword. In a while I passed behind him into the Gents. When I returned he was tapping his teeth thoughtfully with a biro. It was a quarter of an hour after opening time and the regulars had begun to trickle in, braying.

Some weeks later I recognized him at The Woodman and later again at The Prince of Wales, not alone now but in the company of a statuesque brunette with flashing eyes and an excitable manner; the pair of them with a powerful sandy Labrador in tow.

Then one evening at The Prince of Wales this happened. The William Trevor *Doppelgänger* passed me *en route* to the Gents with eyes bulging and gingery hair again upstanding. He gave the impression of advancing always against a headwind, the eyes in his head swivelling. He had what my dear late mother used to call a 'consequential' air about him – meaning up to no good. He was always up to something, being a born plotter. On his way back he greeted me cordially.

'You again,' he said. 'There is someone here whom I'd like you to meet, if you have a moment to spare.' He beckoned me around the corner to where the brunette stood sipping her drink at the curve of the bar, surrounded by admirers.

'Mitzi,' said the gingery man masterfully laying a hand on her bare arm. 'Mitzi, here's a fellow countryman of mine who keeps insisting that I am William Trevor.'

'He is not William Trevor,' said Mitzi, drawing back a step to stare at me, high on the social occasion, high on life.

'My name, what is my name?' said the GM, just like Captain Fluellen.

'I shouldn't be a bit surprised if he *wasn't* William Trevor,' spoke up a non-reader, guffawing into his drink, joined in by Mitzi with her high silvery laugh.

'Perceptive of you, I'm sure,' sneered the GM.

'Perhaps he's *Jack* Trevor Story,' sniggered another.

'*Au contraire*,' replied the GM suavely. Sensing that something momentous had been concluded above his head, the powerful champagne-coloured Labrador seized this opportunity to thrust his damp muzzle into my crotch in a forceful and familiar way, the first but by no means the last of such frontal goosings, amid the general merriment.

'Down, Riley!' they cried. '*Manners!*'

Groaningly Riley subsided. The GM man extended his hand, saying: 'I'm Rory Beamish, of whom you would not have heard, and this lovely lady is Mitzi Kilkelly.'

'Brian,' I said.

They both looked at me, as did Riley from below.

'Anything else?' asked Mitzi.

'Brian Borumna, King of Munster?' said Beamish, tittering into his pint.

'Not a bit like him,' said Mitzi.

'Brian Mallord de Courcey Burke at your service.'

'What a nice name,' said Mitzi brightly.

'Thorpe?' the GM suggested.

'Burke,' I said rather loudly. 'As in Burke and Hare, you know.'

'Oh, *Burke*!' the GM cried. 'Now I get you. What will you have, er, Brian?'

'A White Shield, thank you,' I said.

'*Could* we just have some rapid service here!' Beamish rapping on the counter with the heel of his glass.

The great blond Labrador put down his head and commenced slobbering over his gruesomely distended far-from-private parts.

'*Riles*!' they shouted together, 'be*have*!'

It was through this hedonistic couple that I first met you, on an outing to The George Washington in Belsize village. It was to be a repeat performance of an afternoon when all, as so rarely, had gone well. Beamish picked me up at The Prince, his eyes popping; for he was ever a lover of

130

conspiracy, full of 'sly iniquitee' as Chaucer's fox, very often sodden towards sundown.

'We're going to collect a friend'.

You were Mitzi Kilkelly's friend. Rory's too until I would take you away from him, make you his enemy. We drove to Belsize village in a company car with Wagner blasting from the stereo system and Riley attempting to sing along with his head and shoulders out the window. Beamish had been made redundant but still held on to the car, had gone on the dole. You sat behind me with Mitzi; I had not looked at you as you had come through the gate, feeling my *Schicksal* approaching. I could not place your accent, I could not remember your name. Beamish and Mitzi were laughing their heads off. I remained quiet, feeling you close to me. We drove to The George Washington, passing through the unremitting squalor of Camden Town, Kentish Town, and then Swiss Cottage, all my old haunts.

That I should be smitten by the charms of this slut Sally was in the eyes and sound judgement of the Plantigrade Shuffler an unseemly farce, a fine example of what he called 'emollient irony'. And he was at pains to convey this at the earliest opportunity.

'*En el reino del amor huesped extraño.*' Beamish spoke French, Spanish, with some Norwegian thrown in.

'Whom have we now?' I asked, stumped.

'Master Quevedo. You understand it?'

'Partially.'

'Good.'

Gatting was slowly approaching his first test century or 'ton'. Prodding on the 'off', cutting on the 'leg', pulling to the boundary when he could. All the members were pushing into the Warner's Stand with gin and tonics in hand. Gatting wore a rural sun hat with a floppy brim as if haymaking, not batting for England, and was only thirty short of his 100. But he never made it that day, for Imran was bowling like a man possessed.

Many were of the opinion that the Pakistani captain was a greater 'all-rounder' than bully-boy Botham of Somerset,

131

who (said the silly commentator gentleman in the 'box') had been bowling *well within himself*.

2
Somerset Settle Bed

Her cat sat by the stove. Her hessian dress, as heavy as a cassock, was tied with a belt of blue. She hooked a plastic bucket over her arm. She held a skinned rabbit by its hind legs.

The goodnight kiss could lead to more than that. In their double bed, in your single bed, on the sofa or the settle bed in the kitchen, on a picnic, in the dunes, how long and how ardently when it happened and how often? The old man was a crotch-sniffer, a panty panter, with his sleeves rolled up soaping you in the bath. In your petticoat, in your chemise, in your gymslip. Observing you with his green eyes, lusting after his own flesh and blood, and you reduced to lower than the hired slut, the loose woman, the half-witted slattern in Glastonbury. 'Don't breathe a word of this to your mum.' He should have been castrated with Buddizzo pincers, a remarkable invention by an Italian doctor of genius. Groaning and whispering, 'Not a word of this to your mother, do you hear? Put on your nightie now.'

A crusty bachelor kept savage dogs. One of them flew at you and hung on to your arse growling tenaciously, until Old Parr broke his stick upon its back and off it ran howling.

As a young girl you hung upside down by your legs from a certain tree near Glastonbury, quondam centre of British Christianity, showing off your thighs and knickers, and made a wish. Any wish made while hanging upside down from that tree was sure to come true.

You rode the stallion Jupiter unshod and without bridle in the fields below the Tor. Then you were sixteen years old and working in a coffee shop in Glastonbury, with a half-hour walk home through a park. You were walking home one winter afternoon when the rapist suddenly emerged from ambush and joined you uninvited. 'You are the girl who works in the coffee shop.'

He threw you on the ground and raped you; you struggled and marked his face. You couldn't tell your parents. Mum had known about Dad's carryings-on when you were eight or nine. She had said nothing.

At the age of eighteen you had a pet jackdaw and were in love with David Attenborough.

At the age of nineteen or twenty years you left Glastonbury as a fully fledged *femme fatale* and took a train to London where in no time at all you were being offered drinks on the house by the legendary Compton brothers, Leslie and Denis, lords of The Prince of Wales in Highgate village, being put to bed upstairs, tearing off long strips of wallpaper with your bare fingernails. Of a frolicsome and easy disposition when not down in the dumps, you were frequently high as a kite.

Then, after many adventures, you were Carmencita the hot Spanish or Italian maid visited regularly in your poor attic at night by sweaty Bert the Express Dairy milkrounds-man in blue overalls and peaked cap, climbing through the skylight. On the cheap bedside table a packet of Celtas or Disque Bleu, a bottle of Diamante, two tumblers, a tattered copy of *Oggi*, a small purse with a few pounds in it, a hairclip. I came disguised as the randy roundsman, whispering '*Carmen! Je chante pour moi-même!*' I was Fernando and you Martina, the steamed-up lovers in the *fotonovela*. I was the lion roaring in the pear tree.

'I don't play games,' the not-yet familiar voice said coolly down the line. At the end of the saloon bar in The Angel I had kept two doors under observation and now kept the door of the phone booth ajar and one door under observa-tion. You had promised to come at midday and now it was one-thirty. I had bought two Scandinavian glasses in a hardware shop in Highgate near where I had embraced and bussed you the night before, while Beamish and his lady

134

waited with glasses of brandy in the coffee shop. The heath was five minutes away, the sun was shining, my hopes were high, and now this.

'You can't come out?'

'I *won't* come out,' the voice said calmly. 'As I told you: I don't play games.'

'Who is playing games?'

She had nothing to say to that.

'I am being punished,' I said. 'Is that it?'

'You are being impertinent. And presuming a little, sir. I hardly know you.'

'Who is playing games now?'

She had nothing to say to that. I heard her breathing, listening, the indistinct sounds of her house not five miles away. The silence prolonged itself.

'Well, I suppose I'll see you around,' the voice said airily. As I had nothing to say to that she replaced the receiver and the line went dead.

'No need to get shirty with me, mate.'

'God, he's *aten* it!' called out the flushed Mayoman, delighted at the spectacle of Jack Stack, ever intent on ingratiating himself, swallowing a pint in one go.

'You slags over there,' said a hostile voice that might have been the voice of the estranged husband, Moose himself.

You said to Moose, 'You want to kill me.' Moose said no, not you; it was evident whom he meant. Sometimes you had to sleep with him; it was no good. You made up your own room upstairs; he followed you up. You crept down, slept alone in his room; he followed you down. He was a hundred per cent physical, a Haringey second-row forward, the heavy in the boilerhouse. He began to break things up. You and he could neither part nor live amicably together. It was the classical situation – the Marital Impasse. All concerned were having a bad time. The three children suffered: Saxon, Titus and Liza. The eldest son was twenty-two; Liza had been molested at the age of eight by an artist with a studio in Kentish Town. You knew him. He told me what would happen when you caught him.

You left Moose and went to stay with a redheaded businesswoman who had three redheaded daughters, having left her Jewish husband, a dentist in Golders Green. It is quite rare to meet interesting people in the Golders Green area. Beth Brocklehurst, breathing fire, followed you into her bathroom, sat smoking on the edge of the tub, praised your figure, inquired of your love-life, begged a goodnight kiss. She was attracted to lesbians and ladies with leanings. Her living-room was decorated with posters of sinewy masculine-looking females who had legs long and sinewy as Fanny Blankers Koen's.

Her gardener was a professor whose son had jumped to his death from a tower block. He was a cowed man, his spirit broken, which suited Beth, who treated him like a dog when she didn't treat him like dirt. I encountered this depressed professor in the kitchen, smelling of garden loam and fear, uneasy on the other side of the long table, being patronizingly offered instant coffee. And from the attic window of the former servant's room rented out to you, I watched him moodily raking up pears in the dewy garden below. The house next door was owned by the son of the man who wrote *Gormenghast* and *Titus Groan*.

We were 'married' by the middle daughter Trixie, aged six, in the kitchen. Sixteen rings from a broken white necklace ringed our fingers, our names were repeated. Sally-and-Brian joined and sworn sixteen times; well and truly joined in wedlock by this innocent. Mahaud the Saudi with tribal markings who drank in The Prince had taken us for brother and sister. He was gunman or gardener in a great mansion overlooking Hampstead Heath. Freddy Byswater, the Liverpudlian drunk, embraced you by the serving-hatch. He said that the Irish were only good for digging holes in the road.

You were generous; when your dying mother gave you her own mother's jewellery, you handed it on to Liza. You looked after your mother, slept with her despite the terrible smell, washed her, put her on the pot. She was 'going down like a balloon', shrunken. 'My death comes in a direct line through her.' The old man had moved into the spare room, protesting that he was shy. Your mother had grown sharp; the old man didn't want to watch her dying. She had always been pretty, and now was pretty again; 'making sense at last'. She whispered to you: 'Your children are grown up now . . . Save yourself while you can.'

The long, long delays and then nothing any more; and then, out of the blue, a phone-call. You never said your name, nor mine neither. So you would phone and if one of my sons took the call they would say 'It's Sally'. If Margaret took it she would say sourly 'An admirer'.

We walked down the hill and into Highgate Wood, and up the hill by The Woodman to The Flask and by a shortcut to the ponds. I watched you feeding the ducks on Highgate ponds, dropping grass into the water.

'You don't see me.'

'Of course I see you . . . feeding the ducks.'

No, you insisted, I didn't see you. I protested that I did, not being blind, but you were not mollified.

'I'm watching you,' you said, 'all the time.'

What was one to make of that? With you, I seemed to be further away from you. I could hardly call you my woman, much less my mistress. On good evenings we walked to the top of the hill past the police station, or I waited by The Woodman and you came off the 134 when you were working for the deaf.

'I'm shattered,' you said.

You were frequently shattered.

'I won't live long. I'll die soon. I'm old.'

You remarked on the shortness of my nails. Yours grew and grew, your hair too. Two years ago you told me that you loved me. Me too, I said.

You glared at me.

'Oh no, I won't take that.'

I looked at your hands, fine feminine hands wrinkled at the knuckles, determined hands. You asked me to hold both your hands when you crouched over a narrow trench cut by roadworkers; this was at night behind Fortis Green police station, and I was supposed to whistle. You wore a sort of moss-green-grey T-shirt over the usual loose black fatigues, with Oxfam shoes of a crushed strawberry colour, which you managed to piss over.

I saw the form of a hedgehog run over many times on the dust of the track, and you mentioned cattle-traps of Somerset with hedgehog runs below them. I had to hold both your hands as you leaned back, and I was supposed to whistle, in the dry lane behind The Clissold Arms, a dull, airless very English pub that was like an ocean liner *en route* to India in the 1930s. The lounge was crowded with the undead and their stale cigarette smoke. 'They're not worth saving,' you said, dismissing them.

You were drinking at The Prince of Wales, the back bar of The Alexandra; you were waiting for me there, talking to Big Mike. The estranged husband of Katie 'Buzz' Deering was on speed, jogging in the dark. He asked you to show your breasts; you obliged. You flew into The John Baird, sat on my lap like a bird.

'I have the spondoolicks.'

The unhappy jogger passed. You spent a wet winter's night in the ruins of Alexandra Palace, a foolish thing to do; arrived home with chattering teeth for Moose to throw open the door. He asked no questions, had murder on his mind. We had nowhere to go.

For Moose the footer season opened with fractured ribs, ended with broken teeth. At a rowdy party for rugger friends, all drinking their heads off, he forced you to sit on a hot and hairy lap, the only woman there. A part-time barman 'chatted you up' at The Baird, became aggressive, asked where was the Brain of Britain, demanded attention, kissed you in Beth's kitchen.

'I don't take no from a bird I fancy.'

You told him to go home, that he was pushing his luck. He slunk away, cursing. You took chances, thinking yourself safe in minicabs, asked the coloured driver to kiss you, you were kissing me. He said he was gay; you said it didn't matter, he kissed you. A kerb-crawler drove you home, you changed, were driven to Highgate Golf Club. You asked the fare, but it wasn't even a minicab. You might have been raped. You were moving fast in several directions at once, lost, 'shattered'. Your skin aroma: geranium. Your hair; meadowsweet.

It was around that time that your electricity supply was cut off, and the Falklands débâcle ended. 'The antipodes really grate on me,' a morose drinker admitted at The Gate House. You chased a peeping Tom out of Highgate Wood as if chasing a goose, not a flasher, a flustered biker carrying a white crash-helmet into which he had been masturbating.

'CHRIST IS COMING', went the graffiti on a wall; below it a wit had finely amended, 'WHEN?' and below that another hand had written, 'SO IS TOM (PERRIER)'.

The endless beginning with you; the interminable endings. Thrice at widely separated times (four months) and unsober late at night in someone else's bedroom, you said goodbye, it's impossible. And a fortnight later, two months later, you would phone again, from a French friend's house in Hampstead, from The Star and Garter in Poland Street, calling me out, for a walk, for a drink, for a talk.

One morning in June I received a mysterious phone-call. An unknown voice spoke in my ear: 'Hallo,' said the male voice. 'This is Liam Kelly.'

'Yes, what can I do for you.'

'What can I do for *you*? I'm on the Grace Gate.'

Darkish clouds covered Trent Bridge. I showed you pictures of Imran Khan in action, the handsome Pathan all-rounder, the Pakistani captain. Never in your life had you seen such a handsome man.

'Easy, easy, easy,' chanted the louts before the Lord's Tavern, pints of lager in hand, as Imran Khan moved in to bowl, panther-like.

I was the one who used you and who would abandon you; I was the very worst. 'Wish you could shoot me with your gun,' you said, touching it. 'My breasts are enlarged, now that it's useless.' Where are the charming variations? Where would we be without our atmospherics? One day when we were in the kitchen, drinking white wine on opposite sides of the long refectory table, Buzz came downstairs looking for a comb; came wet from the shower with a small towel about her waist like a sarong, very black and gleaming. Buzz was your best friend; she came from the Windward Islands. She was going out with a West End chef who was half her age, having decided to ditch her husband, who was a relatively wealthy man. He had discovered Buzz on a beach at Barbados.

'Where's the lovely lady?' Big Mike would ask, while polishing a glass. In the morning The Alexandra was generally deserted. Once I spoke to a red-faced man who told me how he had fixed the air-conditioning of a cinema in Mozambique. I told him of the dhows I had seen on the flooded Zambezi and the black monkey chained to a perch in a yard in Mombasa.

Now the urge took hold of us to be away from the habitat of Moose and his henchmen and informers (Freddy the Scouse), going by bus into the country, the hinterland where I had never set foot before. We boarded a bus that turned away from the Barnet route and ended up half an hour later near a police station and a huge pub with a garden at the back; it would have been one of the coach-stops on the great north road out of London, a haunt of highwaymen. On the signboard outside the dole office a hand had painted 'ALEC THE COPPER IS A SPIDER-LOVING CUNT'. We stepped into a great echoing beery pub with food counters and desperate boozers hunched on seats, one fellow in a dirty raincoat taking a pile of old newspapers into the Gents, and in a corner a big throbbing juke box flashing orange lights and out of it a bull voice bellowing. It brought to mind Pabst's movie *Kameradschaft*, the pandemonium with scores of coal-blackened naked miners in the showers, the steam rising up to the roof and the bundles of clothes that resembled hanged men being hauled up and down on chains. Now and again we went there, where I felt relatively

140

unthreatened by Moose and his minions. It was the end of the line.

'Bugger me ol' boots,' a desperate drinker said to no one in particular, 'I'll do that bleeder! So 'elp me.'

'If anyone laid a 'and on Rose, 'ed 'avim.'

'Oh he did, diddee?'

' 'E used to cuddle down wiv' 'er. She thought the world of 'im.'

' 'E wurr a big 'un. R'rrr.'

'That 'e wur.'

In Buzz's place now 'Black Sally' from St Kitts was laughing and shaking all over like a jolly black blancmange, all powerful eighteen stone of her balanced on your lap, crushing you. While busy Buzz Deering was cooking something hot and spicy on the stove we sent out for more white wine.

'Galway Sally', a small beaky-faced woman from Connemara, worked behind the food counter at The Green Man. And no doubt there were other versions of you walking about north London. You were multiplying (or subdividing) yourself. Reality was withdrawing from you, or you from reality.

Once, recovering from a hangover in the afternoon when The Prince had closed, you took me to a friend's place. She was out, the children in the kitchen said, but due back shortly. Molly Gentle came into the bedroom to find us washing each other in the sunken bath. We dressed and went downstairs to the kitchen where she was cooking pancakes. You told of the day when you and she had gone sheep-shearing in the estranged husband's Devon farm, nonplussed the natives who were inclined to sneer at city folk, and fine ladies at that. I walked into Highgate for more Rioja.

This was the good friend who told you later: Any man will do, those with no money who are drunk all the time won't do. After two years apart she returned to her husband.

We went naked to a lower room at Brocklehurst's place,

dragged a double mattress from a spare bed. You asked or rather ordered me to strike you, but I would not. Going downstairs in a sheet, I returned with a tumbler of water and two pears from the garden, where a lion roared in the pear tree each time I had you; but I would not hit you. I was the milkman climbing through the skylight and you the French maid in her poor attic bed.

You had suggested, perhaps frivolously, a honeymoon in Bath, where we would drink at The Hat and Feathers, but we never went to Bath, we never made it. Instead I went to Wandsworth, to keep an eye on the house of friends who had gone to Tuscany (or was it Greece?) on vacation; and to feed their cat, Cecil. It was our ten-day honeymoon there, in Honeywell Road, the whole house seemed to float over the common, over the railway bridge, out over the river, only to come floating back again over The County Arms and The Hope, back to its rightful place, and you and I in it, certainly not in our rightful place.

I went there alone, half hoping you would follow. The whole house took to creaking and groaning in the August heatwave, the woodwork continuing to contract and expand, to the accompaniment of a Rastafarian uproar in a house down the way. Next door an irate mother's voice spoke to a child: 'Come on, *sit up* and eat properly!' This into my ear. In the heat the walls had become paper-thin. I heard the child complain. 'You're going to get a *smack on the bottom*!' cried the mother, her patience sorely tried. Then the phone rang. It was midnight, maybe later. Then came the smack and the screams of the child.

'Sally is that you?'

'Dieter here,' said an alert unsober foreign male voice.

'Who?'

'Dieter,' the brisk foreign voice said, 'from Hamburg, you know. How are you *meek*? Happy birthday!'

'Who are you? Is this your idea of a joke?'

'Dieter,' the unsober foreign voice said. 'Dieter here *meek*. You are not *meek*?'

'No,' I said. 'I am *not* meek, damn you, whoever you are!'

I heard a buzzing and babble of confused voices and then the Dieter voice came clear.

'Who is this please?'

I thought about this. It was 2.10 a.m.

'Baron Hubert von Bechtolsheim,' I said, replacing the receiver.

The hot sun shone all next day but you did not come. I bought drink and provisions. The cat Cecil was infested with fleas, bluebottles hummed above the cat-dish. Rasta music started up as darkness fell. I did not venture out, thinking that you might arrive and find the house empty. At six you phoned. I gave you the address and directions how to get there. You were non-committal. 'I *miss* you.'

I retired to bed at midnight, unsober, having drunk half a bottle of gin and one bottle of chilled Muscadet, dining lightly on corncobs. The house continued creaking and groaning. In the middle of the night the bell chimed briefly below and I was awake at once and heard you call my name through the letterbox, heard the engine throb of a minicab outside. I descended three flights of stairs, opened the front door, and there you were, with a minicab behind you and a West Indian driver rolling down the window.

'That's it then, miss?'

'That's him,' you said. 'Goodnight. Thanks.' He let in the clutch and drove away as you came into the hall to be embraced.

'I have arrived,' you said, 'so to speak.'

'Come in,' I said.

Juggernauts were weakening Hammersmith Bridge. Suspension chains had been slackened and iron studs collapsed in one of the towers. The bridge had slipped two-and-a-half inches and no more traffic was allowed over.

The body of an unidentified man had been found wrapped in curtain material in an East End rubbish tip. Also died this year: Rita Hayworth, my old heart-throb, William Powell, Hollywood actor, Alex Trocchi, writer and reformed junky, Rinty Monaghan, flyweight boxer, Thorold Dickinson, film director, William Empson, poet, Tommy Cooper, comedian.

143

*

We were circling Buzz's big living-room on the sanded floor near the patio flooded with sun through the louvred blinds, as if we were dancing in Barbados, the big portable machine throbbing and blinking all its lights with 'Loving You', when the three kids came running quickly in to strike at our private parts with the backs of their hands, even the girl (normally silent and thin, not eating), giggling.

'Having it off,' they said. (''E's 'aven it orff wiv 'er, see.')

'Where are all the charming variations?' they asked.

On a moonlit night in August on Lake Windermere.

'Come off it,' they said.

We went again to Athene's, that Ali Baba's cave, and Stavros the owner gave us drinks on the house because his wife Mary was pregnant, and he wanted a son.

'A glass of wine then, to put us in the proper frame of mind.'

Stavros insisted that it had to be Greek brandy.

'Go on, have a little taste.'

We said we would. The sexual assistant came and lit the candle on our table and you told me of Sam and Annie Loveridge, aged one hundred and two and ninety-nine respectively, who lived with their eldest boy Jack aged seventy-seven in a mobile home in a field near the village of Curry Rivel, adjacent to Langport in Somerset. Everybody lived to a ripe old age in Somerset. The signs in nature were for a good summer. Stavros came and sat with us.

'What do you pair do in the daytime?'

He worked long hours, worked hard, intended to return to Greece and buy property. London was 'unreal'. He ordered more Greek brandy. You looked at me with your lynx-green eyes under the bang of hair like a strange animal in the mouth of its burrow – *stilly crouches she*. Stavros said we must come to his place on Thursday nights when all the Greeks were there.

'What happens?'

'Belly-dancing.'

*

144

'My friend is in a shocking state,' was a preamble I had heard more than once. (You had a Jewish friend who laid out corpses). Dr Peggy Sayers had a husband who drank. He was a surgeon and he drank whisky, and presently went mad. He wore all his clothes, even to an overcoat and cap, in bed, had forgotten who he was, did not recognize his wife. He had to be put away. He had premature senile dementia, didn't know where he was. She was advised not to visit him.

She met a bearded fellow of eighteen years of age, lived with him, then they got married. Now she was fifty-five and he twenty-five and looked the same age.

Then the husband recovered. He remembered his past but not the mental home, his wife was happily married, he was resigned. Dr Sayers was an eye-specialist at Moorfields Eye Hospital. Nava Jahans taught French in a school in Hampstead, wept buckets in The Prince one night, because her boyfriend had left her. He didn't like the Irish.

'I made a complete horlicks of it,' you said. Your stories tended to be on the grim side; was this the famous city edge? You came breezily into the sitting-room off the kitchen where Beamish and Mitzi 'relaxed', and told how Brixton police had ganged up on one black man, and you wouldn't have it, you stuck up for him, gave cheek to the police. 'Oh so you are one of them too?' the copper sneered, perhaps mistaking you for a darkie. You were dark as an Ethiopian beauty with esoteric green eyes, the dark hair combed down over the eyes; and on your face tribal markings, a sign of caste and valour. Mitzi slammed the car door in your face, so you had a healed scar on the bridge of your nose, and would presently require five stitches in your chin, from an unsober accident in Buzz's garden. Testimony to the bottle.

You came wet and naked out of the sea at night and some Spanish fishermen were watching you dressing behind a wall and going into a *merendero* and ordering coffee and *anís seco* as the sun came up and you lit a Celtas.

You told of the fellow from Yorkshire who liked girls three in a bed, with *Playboy* centrefold nudes tacked on the wall.

145

Nava wanted you to join her in a sauna and 'Mrs Bracegirdle' rather fancied you. We smoked your hash in the kitchen and I was dismembering a chicken and cutting it up on the breadboard and you were watching me and called out *'I can't stand it any more!'* and we went to bed and I had you twice. And then you told me that Mary Queen of Scots had her favourite Skye terrier hidden under her crinoline as she knelt at the block and when her head dropped into the basket the terrier flew out, at Fotheringhay, at Fotheringhay.

Contradictions abounded.

Beamish was a master of circumlocution. He had written a thriller, now he was writing a book about the gold standard, and it would 'make a mint'. He mixed lethal Silver Bullets in the kitchen, studied the *Economist* and *Financial Times* in the living-room, where several cats glided in and out or stared through the window at Riley slumped on the floor. We drank on either side of the round table. The picture above us framed behind glass was an illustration torn from the Bible: *'The great fish vomiting out Jonah upon the dry land'*. We sat there, drinking and talking, waiting for Mitzi to return from work.

'Shouldn't be at all surprised . . . . Something is *sure* to turn up. Something damn well better turn up!' When unsober Beamish retreated to the black leather sofa, became the Autocrat issuing ultimatums. Those ever-paranoid eyes of his studied me, his freckled features broke up into extraordinary convulsions, the eyes widening, the hair standing on end.

'What about another Silver Bullet?'

Beamish no longer received the dole. The labour exchange people said he was over-qualified. The jobs that might suit him were just not coming up. He had French, some Spanish and Norwegian, kept *au courant* with fluctuations on the stock exchange, had been a learned economist, and liked to adopt a sanguine air. Something would turn up, but in the meantime Mitzi could support him. There were a number of cats at Grand Avenue as well as the voracious Riley; Mitzi could support them all.

'The Eskimos have thirty-eight different words for snow,' Beamish said.

'I wonder how many different words for sand the Arabs have.'

Life at number 64 continued on its own sweet way.

Technically you had lost your virginity at the age of four when you took a tumble off your tricycle. Your marriage was not a success. Your women friends were all divorced and all had gentle names of women one could trust: Molly Gentle, Sue Ainsley, Cheryl Bailey of the Caribbean, the Russian Nava Jahans, Geraldine Quinn, and a desperate Polish woman whom we had met one day in The Rose and Crown.

When let off the leash Riley became demented; freedom went to his head. At the cricket pitches in Highgate Wood he began quartering the ground, muzzle down and powerful shoulders working, backtracking and then disappearing among the trees, followed by Beamish in a highly exasperated mood. '*Rile-eeeee!*'

Riley went coursing through the wood, depositing steaming hot stools at every gate. Rushing down the hill he came upon a frail old woman out exercising her aged golden retriever, an animal as old and frail as the mistress. But soon Riley was gambolling about this pair, sniffing and canoodling, instantly aroused and attempting to mount the aged retriever dog, made dizzy by these avid attentions. With much trouble Beamish got Riley back on the leash, no sooner connected than dragged forcefully up the hill and out through the west gate. Riley, Mitzi said, was a handful; she never attempted to control him on the lead. It fell to Beamish to exercise the brute, which he did morning and evening. I would come upon the great steaming stools by the gates and would move with circumspection, heading for The Prince, or The Angel, or The Gate House.

Love Goes A-Riding (Your Well-Deserved Garter)

A pregnant schoolgirl goes missing from a Cornish fishing village. A body is recovered, but not the right one. Are these two incidents connected?

We love what is imperishable, that other body perceived as being imperishable (the old lie). The reflection of your face in the window at Grand Avenue opening on the garden, with the children at the bonfire. Your dear face amid the children.

Later, making do, and no wiser, we love what is perishable; the other body rising and sinking like a corpse in the sea. But you would always remain the same age for me: a good-looking thirty-nine that could pass for six years younger. So you would never grow any older, provided I left you, provided we parted, preserving each other in aspic.

You were The-Tart-Over-the-Hill, The-Easy-Lay, The Flibbertigibbet, The Good-Fuck, The Woolworth's Girl, in Margaret's considered terms of opprobrium.

'I have an Arts Degree,' you said tartly, 'more than she has – the stuck-up bitch!' Margaret Burke, A Stuck-Up Bitch.

All for a bit of slap-and-tickle. All for a bit of fun; for my girl's a Somerset girl, tiddleybum, tiddleybum. We having begun our half-life together in others' gardens, terraces and kitchens, living-rooms and spare bedrooms; over an area that grew progressively wider to embrace not only Hampstead but Finsbury Park and the fringes of Crouch End and Barnet, covering say a twenty-mile radius. And when you lay down in the sun in bra and panties the peeping Toms crept forth, holding their breaths, to tiptoe past; the eager

148

voyeurs alertly observant on the slopes of the hill in Ken Wood or Hampstead Heath overlooking the ponds.

Beamish had returned in a particularly sour mood from vacation in Cornwall and was soon putting it about at 64 Grand Avenue that our Sal was no better than she should be, but 'loose', and 'immoral', much too friendly with 'underworld types', a 'foot-fetishist', no less. What he meant to say was: Not my type, old man. What he meant was: Thick. Our consorting in the bath, under the shower and in the toilet puzzled him.

You had gone home for warmer clothes. Moose saw you in the bath with enlarged breasts, tufts of shameless hair under your arms, and dared to question you. He gave you penetrating looks and said *you* looked younger and prettier, must have been with a hundred men. You said nothing to that, spoke to your children, collected some clothes, phoned a minicab and again departed, leaving poor Moose speechless.

Nick Ridley at The Prince was 'into bondage', had strung up a Chinese girl, cut her down before she choked. He was not 'into verbals', but loved to hear the Monday night band play 'Georgia'. He had put the frighteners on some pushy East Ender, got into a bundle, done him in, was put away for manslaughter. Slip him a hundred quid and he'll give you the low-down, Beamish said, who had noticed that a young whore was working the lunchtime trade at The Baird. Blow-jobs and hand-jobs in company cars, according to the observant Beamish. Drop him the hundred, Beamish said, and see what he'll say.

Riddled with Silver Bullets one night had he not asked Mitzi to dress up in fishnet stockings and red garters, black patent leathers with six-inch stiletto heels, a wet-look plastic mackintosh, and awoke sober next morning to find this apparition sleeping by his side? The dark eyeliner had run, the false eyelashes were awry, the stilettos had penetrated the wet-look mac. Beamish sprang out of bed, demanding to

know what the fucking hell was this supposed to mean.
  Your fancy, dear heart. Only your fancy.

You were scandalized by the gyrations of the English belly-
dancer in the candlelit basement at Athene's. You told me
so. I sat beside you among the Greeks and drank Greek
brandy. Stavros sang in a velvety voice and they all laughed
and applauded. Then the lights were turned off and on came
the belly-dancer. She was as wanton and buxom as could be
desired, showing off her bowspring back, her tufted armpits,
the sweat of her brow. Stavros stuffed a fiver into her
cleavage to encourage the rest, and soon bra and panties
were abulge with fivers and tenners, and she gyrated in the
candlelight like a Pict girl festooned with pagan feathers.

You told me your dream. You were climbing a hill with me.
There was the sound of stones rattling; splashings from
above, gurglings from below, on this rain-sodden mountain
We came upon a spring of water that gushed out from under
a thicket and then saw an elephant, dripping wet, washing
itself there, using its trunk as a hose. As we approached the
elephant turned itself into an ape.
  One day you said: 'I dreamt you turned into a tree.' And
another day: 'I dreamt you came in my hair.' And another
day again: 'I dreamt you were a tree between my legs.'
  'I had a dream too,' I said. We were wandering from room
to room in this curious house of interleading rooms like
*Berlinzimmer*s all empty or oddly furnished. We went down
the wide stairs into a room with tall windows. Again and
again I had dreamed of this vaguely disturbing place, called
'Bullsease', or 'Haus Herzentodt'. I was there as usual,
waiting for you, nervous and anxious. Then I am outside,
and coming towards me a sort of hay wagon of Somerset
packed with long-stemmed flowers splendid as fountain
spray. An oldish countrywoman with a bandana knotted
about her head is holding the reins, but there is no horse
between the shafts, the wagon packed with flowers moves
slowly and grandly over the stubble.
  I saw your dear face to one side, leaning out; and then I

150

was again inside and you approached with a gift of flowers, 'flowershod and swaying', breathless, your face not quite your true face but a mixture of Hannelore of Berlin and the Manx girl Thea Craine of long ago.

We found ourselves in a narrow corridor. You suggested: 'Best meet her.' We passed a group of people pressed to the wall, smiling. We went into the kitchen and Margaret was there with her friend Betsy Arbuckle. I walked around the table, having forgotten Betsy's name, said 'Nancy', and made a gesture of metaphysical liquidation. Margaret was freezingly polite.

After a short and uncomfortable time, Margaret silent and staring, Betsy gushing, you made an excuse to leave the room. I followed you. In 'our' room we were instantly undressed and I pulled you down by the window. 'There's moisture down below,' you said. There was indeed. 'One of Mother Nature's little secrets,' you said. I had you *a tergo* under the window.

There were houses and flats opposite, but neither of Berlin nor of Somerset, let alone the Isle of Man; just uncomfortable-looking dream dwellings. It was late evening and electric lights were shining. In a dressing-gown and in a mood of *post coitum triste* I went out to unplug or disconnect these lights that were shining into the room. I unplugged a number of them, but one persistent light remained, the source of which I could not find. I came to a Spanish bar. The drinkers were all male, with their back to me, watching some game on television.

Ken Shorland-Ball, DSO, usually drank on his own, studying the clouds passing over Cromwell's house in Pond Square. He was not given to boasting; his thoughts always seemed to be fixed upon the past, the days of active service. On a moonlit night he had pranged two Dorniers over Hackney Marsh. A friend of his in Bomber Command had told him of Jerry fighters playing *Schlagermusik* with their machine-guns all along the bellies of Wellingtons from cockpit to tail-gun and the big clumsy bombers on fire, keeling over and the crew parachuting out. The German bombers came up the river to set fire to the docks.

*

Beamish was now frequently to be seen in The John Baird drinking pints of Directors' and talking to Alec Diggs, a former member of the Spanish International Brigade. An ex-postman from Mayo, a Gaelic speaker and reader of *An Béal Bocht*, drank with them. From him Rory earned for himself the sobriquet *Eoghan Ruadh an Bheil Bhinn* or Red-Rory-of-the-Sweet-Mouth. This was Liam who worked on the Grace Gate at Lord's during test matches.

'Outside Tralee one time . . .' I heard the great raconteur say as I sidled in. He invited me to join them and ordered up a drink.

'How am I?' he said. 'Absolutely bloody well fed up to the back teeth.'

'The pound sterling rock steady and Glaxo shares up,' said Mitzi, tossing her head like a gollywog.

'Is *dolor* masculine or feminine? You would know, Alec,' said Red Rory. '*Angustia* is feminine, I believe. Anyway what's the difference?'

'The difference between grief and pain,' Alec said. 'You can't have a physical *angustia*. It's anxiety more than pain.'

'A pain in the arse?'

'Back again all bright and bushy-eyed are we?' said the intolerably gregarious barman. 'Same again then?'

'Must dash', Mitzi said rising up. 'Things to be done *Byeeee!*'

'I shouldn't be in the least surprised if you weren't William Trevor at all,' I said to Beamish who was staring fixedly at the door through which Mitzi had passed.

'Well, you may set your mind at rest,' he said, 'because I'm not.'

'What's Madame doing?'

'Part-time kindergarting, to keep me in the style I have grown so accustomed to,' said Beamish, applying his lips to his foaming Directors'.

'And ever-loyal Riley?'

Beamish put down his depleted pint and threw himself back in his seat, extending his right arm.

'The good Riley is at home, since you are kind enough to

inquire, guarding our possessions. He has pulled this arm right out of its socket.' The Plantigrade Shuffler veering wildly from side to side, dragged hither and thither by Riley, 'luffing' in the manner of the insane butcher in Buñuel's *El.* The powerful champagne-coloured Labrador dragging him off his feet.

recalled the hens scratching about The Drunken Duck public house and sailing on Lake Windermere by night under a sickle moon, fishing for char, listening to Villa-Lobos on the car radio as we waited for the ferry, Bill Swainson and , and the trout rising on the lake at night and phosphorescent bubbles from the wake of the little yacht and the sickle moon breaking up into several moons. And walking over the fells to come to the Bridge Inn that Sunday, and ineffable melancholy mixed with joy, rare as hot sun on an April day, rarer than radium, missing you, but also knowing you were somewhere (in Glastonbury) thinking of me. And drinking the good Thwaites draught ale at The Masons, and the hut by the lake.

You came like the wind from Glastonbury, driven at 95 mph on the M4 by Murchison. A pebble flew up to shatter the windscreen which turned opaque but Murchison thrust his gloved fist through it and drove on, a regular Stirling Moss. And you went from pub to pub trying to find me, pursued by an unsober Dubliner from The Red Lion and gun. You were in a minicab, were quite pleased that I was 'so hard to find'; until coming into The Alexandra you found me with Verschoyle.

Bill's friend Miles Fielding had driven me from Windermere to Preston at 80 mph and I caught the London train with minutes to spare. Two Chinese girls gabbled all the way to Euston. When I was leaving I asked Swainson if I could have invited you. Of course, he said. I had not thought to ask, having been rebuffed by the wife of a friend in Surrey to whom I had facetiously described you as 'a loose woman'.

'I *missed* you,' you said. It was a recurring refrain. And what was Murchison doing in Glastonbury?

'Say something nice.'

I had missed you on Lake Windermere by the boathouse in early August, a month of falling stars; naked in the stream at Calne in Wiltshire in the converted mill-house mentioned in the Domesday Book; and in a wheatfield at Battle in Sussex, all in one summer.

We did not drink together in the evening at Ye Dumb Post Inn nor listen to the stout publican Brian Pitt boast 'This is a madhouse'; nor at night listen to the millrace nor smell the summer fields nor hear the bongo-drum boys effing and blinding under the harvest moon over the Marden; nor did you retire to bed with me.

Margaret had said: 'Don't look, I'm undressing.' So I looked out the window. Then: 'No, I'm not.' She came down the retractable ladder in pyjamas the colour of *eau de Nil*, asking: 'Why do I feel so wretched in the morning?'

For us there was no *Kleines Schäferstundchen*.

You would come nude as Eve, up to your knees in the stream under the stand of Victoria plums; the provocative roll of a fighting ship, heavy-cannoned. A hot number *loco en la cama*. A touch of lubricity. More than a touch.

'Say something nice to me.'

'I dreamt I was in Acapulco with a boring old woman. It was so green and warm.'

She had her bottom pinched by Chuck Berry at a party after a gig. 'Nice ass,' said Chuck gallantly.

'I dreamt I was made managing director of Irish Cement.'

Another dream: You were invited to Sandringham to meet Prince Charles. In a cottage somewhere on the estate the queen approached in jodhpurs and an orange jersey and her first words were: 'I'm afraid we seem to have an enormous lot of dogs here.'

The place was full of dogs, chows, corgis. Prince Charles' face appeared behind a sofa; he struggled to his feet, stood up to shake your hand. 'I *knew* I was right. I thought it was you.'

'Seen close to he is better-looking than the photos suggest. The ears don't stick out quite as much and the jaw is less lantern. He is in fact quite a handsome man. His opening shot was most diplomatic. He took my arm and led me aside to ask: "*Do* I recognize you?"

'Impeccable timing. Then we had tea with the queen and all the royal dogs.'

Another dream: you dreamt that you had breakfast with Prince Charles. Or rather you watched him eating his breakfast. An enormous butler's tray was brought to him on a trolley, and plate after plate put down before him, cups of tea, two fillets of kipper nicely arranged, a couple of big bangers, marmalade and toast, a portion of kedgeree. He ate it all quite calmly and didn't think to offer you any. By this time he was formally dressed in a grey suit and highly polished black shoes, none of your casual dressing-gown and slippers for Charles, to whom all this was quite normal, something he did every morning, served by his butler, being watched by an admirer and it just never occurred to him to offer you anything, 'although I was starving'. The butler was 'just a hand serving the heir to the English Throne. I was nothing.

'Then Wales took me for a stroll about the estate. The queen had gone off with her dogs and we were alone. Then he took my arm again and said: "There is something I must show you." We went indoors again and on his private projector he ran a film which he thought I might like – *Bahama Passage* with Sterling Hayden and Madeleine Carroll up to no good on an isle underneath the sea that was mysteriously flooded with perpetual sunlight. Before that they were in a city and she took off her stockings behind a screen.

'Then I was walking with my father along a path. He was smoking a Woodbine and said in a very sour way: "Well, *you*'ve earned your Garter."'

'You don't see me,' were your accusing words. I was standing on a knoll watching you feeding grass to the ducks on Highgate pond, the ducks ignoring this food, circling about, quacking.

'Certainly I see you,' I said, 'feeding ducks.'

'He's been a bad husband to me,' you said of Moose, adding as an afterthought: 'But then again I've been a bad wife to him.'

For months at a stretch you went underground, did not contact me, I could not phone you. Then one fine morning you came strolling over the brow of the hill by The Swiss Chalet, carrying a string bag with French bread and cucumber, a Penguin book (*Querelle of Brest*). We went down the hill into The Royal Oak. You had painted two white fishes head-to-head on your brown Russian boots, it was our astrological sign, Pisces, the furtive ones. I showed you my passport photo and you took it, hid it in one of the Russian boots. You had been to Dorset, chauffeur for your father Victor Nutt, stopping in the pretty village of Langton Herring. Victor Nutt was smoking a Woodbine. He looked around, asked: 'Why have you taken me here?'

You repeated once again that we were finished. 'Find another,' you said.

I said nothing to that. You touched my knee.

'Find somebody else,' you said. 'Live with a man.'

You had been to a gathering of gays in a club near Marble Arch. They were all smoking pot, got up in black leather like shining beetles. A Harley Davidson was hung up on chains and they were raffling it. The winner had to sing a song. He came up to the platform waving his winning ticket and sang the old George Shearing number 'The Nearness Of You'. All the black-clad gays cheered. Later one of them bit your arse, twice. Another goosed you.

'You are my one and only,' I said. 'Am I not yours?'

The gays were drinking from six-packs, Budweiser and Schlitz, behaving in a truculent manner adopted from their heroes, Brando, Bronson, Clint Eastwood. You sat behind a curtain with a friendly gay. The floodlit motorbike hung on chains. 'Bud?' a gay said. 'I'm stone-mad for it.'

'I am turning into you.'

'Then I'll turn into you.' I said.

You told of a male friend who dressed in drag, went to parties got up as Shirley Bassey, called herself 'Shirley'.

mimed to Bassey songs, wanted to be her, would-be Bassey
the torch-singer of Tiger Bay, bursting out of a sheath dress
with shoulders bare.

Butterflies can alter their wing patterns to make themselves more like their beloved, by and by, in the by-and-by.
That studied languor of the bared flesh, the dark eyes aglitter
under the 1920s fringe, fitful gleams of rings and pendants in
the spotlight that moved as she moved. No period for feeling
lachrymose.

> *Deare, if you change, I'll never chuse againe,*
> *Sweet; if you shrink . . .*

The waning sunlight bounced off Veronese-green wallpaper
and the burnished copper trays hung as wall decorations by
the toilets in The Alexandra where we sat.

'I feel I'm turning into a man,' you said.

A brute with a great belly was playing the fruit machines,
'THE RACE AGAINST TIME' emblazoned across his chest.

'If you do I'll turn into a woman,' I said.

'Perhaps you should live with a man?'

Wally the collector of matchboxes crouched over his
drinks, halves of draught Smithwick's followed by a glass of
Campari like blood in his glass, sunken in thought.

'It's nice if you can feel a bit bettah . . .' a voice said.

'Shut your bleedin cake'ole.'

'New marble is always right.'

'Made a complete horlicks of it.'

Now closing time had come around again and they were
calling out 'Time, please!' and you said we might as well go
to Athene's for some Greek brandy, which we did, being
warmly received once more by Stavros himself.

'Don't give a monkey's.'

'No bleeden wey, guv.'

Having another go at staying off the bottle,' your voice at
the end of the line said confidentially. 'Then fell off the
wagon with the hell of a crash. Got so bad for a week it's a

wonder I didn't drown. No guts you see.' (Pause.) 'What did you say?'

'Nothing,' I said.

'Feel so frantic and alone,' the voice at the end of the line resumed. (Longish silence.) 'Look for you everywhere.' (Low) 'Talk about you to everybody.' (Longer pause, lower) 'What's that supposed to mean?' (Silence, emphatic) 'I *miss* you.' (Long silence.) 'What was that?'

Sound of receiver being replaced to muffled curse. When we met again you told me you had drunk about two hundred glasses of wine at The Railway Tavern in Finsbury Park and 'broke the place up'.

'Get sorted out,' they said.

You drank until you were cleaned out, feeling 'knackered', and again went to ground.

I had asked you not to leave it so long and you promised you would not. If I cannot have you, can I at least have your photograph? On Axminster station one day in August of the previous year, looking very brown and Mediterranean, not posing but staring at the photographer (Moose?), returning from family outing to Lyme Regis. You looked grave.

Now rain fell like hailstones, white drops falling out of the sky, and Buzz driving off with her kids as I approached the flat.

Nothing since the first of February and now June 25th and still nothing, four months' abstinence, not quite that for you; Moose still fancies you, perhaps still loves you, wants to murder me. Then I saw you twice in seven months, had you twice in seven months, and both drunk each time. Once you were 'infected', once 'pregnant', and always missing me. The sun enters Cancer on the 21st. For one reason or another it appears to be strained relationships and uncertainty about the future. This cycle must end. I phoned Buzz and asked for your Glastonbury number, which you had urged me never to use, phoned that number and found myself speaking to an affable lady in Loch Ness, in cold far-off Scotland.

'How's the monster?'

Brief guffaw.

'He is very seasonable.'

'Sorry to trouble you. I seem to have the wrong number.'

'No trouble at all,' Loch Ness said brightly and hung up. Glastonbury did not respond. Perhaps you were out at Chewton Mendip entertaining the Nutts. On television Sir Harry Secombe got up in a blazer stood before the Wells Choir and the ballsy guys in blue blazers sang lustily 'The Fires of Love Die'.

You did not write, phone, or walk in the Broadway. Buzz thought you were still in Somerset. Distance is the prequisite of happiness, some German (Eich Ehrgeiz?) thought perversely. I went on waiting, unhappily.

'All he ever wanted of her was a large hot meal every night, back-rubs in the bath and his rugby gear washed every Friday,' Buzz said, laughing.

'And his jockstrap,' I suggested.

Buzz screeched.

'But it's *you* she loves. She can't stop talking about you.'

I saw a brute whom I took to be Moose head-butting a terrified drinker outside the Eastern Electricity showrooms on the Broadway one night. If not getting thoroughly pissed on vodka in The Railway Arms he was stepping into The Alexandra by one door as I left by the other, walking up and down East Finchley, and what if I met him? Felled by a pile-driver in the breadbasket and castrated with a breadknife.

I took to drinking with the Mystical Meath Man in The Alexandra. He had a number of bank accounts and was overdrawn on all of them. He advised me to spend three days and nights neither drinking, smoking nor eating in Glenmalure. He came from Navan, was doing some work on a house in Collingwood Avenue for Trimmer whose sister had a heart attack, aged twenty-seven.

'Surely a bit early for that?' I said.

'You can have a heart attack at any age,' Trimmer said.

'Pigs that eat out of fires, goats that drink their own piss, calves born all the year round,' said the MMM, 'that's Cavan,' burying his nose in his pint.

'So did Sarah Miles,' I said. 'Does still for all I know. Drink

159

her own piss I mean. Said to be terribly good for the health,
but you must drink it fresh and steaming hot. Can't leave it
standing around.'

'Well,' said the MMM, 'that beats cock-fighting.'

'Good for the goats,' I said. 'And Sarah Miles.'

'Ever been to The Frog and Parrot in Sheffield?'

'Never set foot in those parts,' I said.

'There's a publican there who brews a beer of about
seventeen per cent alcohol in his cellar.'

'In The Frog and Parrot?'

'The very place.'

'Grand name for a pub.'

'Would you chance another?' said the MMM smoothly.

'Would a duck swim?'

You said we 'might as well pack it in'; for our 'lack of the
readies' was chronic.

Where, then, was our cottage small by a waterfall? In a
time of heart-scalding and promises denied.

You would settle into the driving seat, light up a cigarette,
and drive off to Blandford Forum, or Chaldon Herring, or
Maiden Newton, or Litton Cheney, or Cerne Abbas in Dorset
or Slough's Despond or some small village in the Mendip
Hills, haunt of adders.

You were giving me a long reflective stare, a horse-eyed
look under your bangs, saying nothing, your tipped cigarette
on the lip of the ashtray, your pint a third depleted.

'I dreamt you came in my hair.'

Not in Lyme Regis nor in Chuffnell Regis. There stood the
empty cottage; behind it the beach with driftwood.

'Where did you get those lovely moleskin trousers?'

'There wasn't a day down there in Wiltshire when I didn't
think of you,' I said.

The clatter of the millrace, a spider's web in the centre of
the mill-wheel, the rattle of the wren every morning, the
murmur of the Marden. I brought out a cast-iron garden
chair, stuck it in the stream, sat in it naked, read Prescott's
Conquest of Mexico, felt your absence. A minnow gulped down
a wasp under the plum tree where waterlogged snails lay on

the clay bed and warble-flies traversed the stream a foot wide where the heron had left its careful tracks.

'What do you mean,' you said, 'a day? Why not every minute?'

The sweet pealing of the church bell in Bremhill where Margaret (a great mislayer of things) had lost her pocket-book with all her holiday money, later reclaimed from some honest person; the choked-off cry of the pheasant and the birds calling '*Refrain, refrain, refrain*' to the eddies in the pool. Sunlight on leaves reflecting water, a stand of Victoria plums: ecstatic awareness.

'Why not indeed.'

You wrote from Glastonbury, a postcard showing the famous Tor in moonlight, discreetly sealed within an envelope. 'Dear Brian, It's raining and cold and the wind blows and the journey was beastly full of delays. I shall either come back immediately or stay longer than I had intended. Otherwise the air is fresh and the people friendly. Your Sally.'

In great warehouses in Glastonbury and in the Mendips, farmhouse Cheddar is slowly getting older and riper and stronger, wrapped in film and packed in wooden cases stored on well-ventilated shelves with two-inch cheesecloth protecting the perimeter, looked after by old cheese-makers with cheese-bores in hand, gripped in yellow rubber gloves, testing and crumbling the cheese, inhaling it, something good to write home about alright.

4
Calne, Wilts (Absences)

She needs to humiliate herself in order to save him. There's no wind at all. A gorgeous full moon rises. The fishing boats return to their anchorage at sundown. He walks along the shore.

Ye Dumb Post Inn. 'Did get leg over last night, Seth?' 'Nay, but tell thee what though: I get a better ride off tractor than ah do off t'Missus.'

I went down there with Margaret on *her* invitation, for a long weekend at the beginning of August, in a month of falling stars. We were lucky with the weather.

Walked out the first morning onto the Nature Trail which commenced with a large fresh human turd steaming on the middle of the path, not long discharged and a-hum with frantic bluebottles. Ten minutes later I all but trod on a rabbit dying of cruel myxomatosis, its head down, shuddering in agony. The path followed the Marden stream as it flowed under an antique humpbacked bridge and then across a road, and I could smell the toxic land and presently heard the grinding and screeching of industrial machinery as acetylene sparks flew from a dark open door. A woman out walking her dog bade me the time of day as we passed.

Returning I found a pool deep and wide enough to dip in dressed and saw the familiar herd of Jerseys crossing a field and on approaching Hazeland Mill thought or imagined I saw whom but Margaret walking to meet me and waving but a closer view revealed this as my washed white shirt flapping on the line.

A hairy-chested fellow in a string vest called out that it was his birthday and he was buying the bar drinks. He had a cleft palate and seemed a little half-witted, a Viking who had lost his way. Some drank from pewter mugs, a fellow with one finger on his right hand, all tattooed fellows in T-shirts, then a smiling Negro appeared in shorts. A big solid lump of a man worked the pumps, affable to regulars, and this was Brian Pitt the genial host. An old timer carried in a hand-cranked gramophone and set it to play some old favourites. Margaret and I sat by the window and saw a harvest moon rise over a distant hill and sheep moved around in a misty field as Richard Tauber sang '*O Bella Margherita*' as though he were singing under the sea.

'A trip down Memory Lane,' the old man said. He put it all together again and departed.

We left the pub in the Wiltshire dusk and went down a hill by a field of peaceful sheep grazing in moonlight.

By Drewett's Mill a signpost pointed towards BATH 5 MILES. Tourists gazed at objects on the abbey walls and a bare-shouldered lady who might as well have been in a museum, being edified by what she saw.

'The faithless wandering about,' Margaret said, 'faith-lessly.'

A gold filling fell out of my back molar as I bought two cornets of ice-cream and a carillon of bells rang out right merrily as we departed from Bath. Passing through Chippenham on the way back Margaret drove several times about a roundabout in Speen (Spleen?) while looking for a route to London, her temper becoming less and less sweet as we drove round and round.

'You are supposed to be the map-reader.'

Don't look now. When love begins to sicken and decay it useth an enforced ceremony.

Across the bar a young father dandled a baby on his lap, put it in the crook of his arm, gave it the bottle, all to a song by Joan Armatrading, in The Angel, Islington, where Margaret and I had gone for one last drink on our return from Wiltshire. The infant made cooing sounds, jerking out its bootees. Beyond them a window seemed to open on a blue sky but I knew darkness had already fallen, and the blue sky was a colour television screen where presently a line of burnt-out double-decker buses appeared and then earnest demonstrators marching with banners through Belfast. Margaret sat silent with her gin and tonic, tired by the long drive home. The barman pushed small change towards me.

'You're away over the top, mate.'

'Blame it on travel fatigue,' I said, pocketing the coins.

Back from Wiltshire and the phone rang twice. I assumed it was Beamish on the razzle and answered the second call with circumspection. You said my name rather loudly.

'How are the eyes?'

'Alright. It's the teeth now. I lost one in Bath.'

'In the *bath*!'

'No, in Bath.'

'What were you doing in Bath?'

'Oh passing through, you know.'

The shire once lauded by Camden now sunken in apathy and sloth, in the force of inertia as defined in mechanics. It was on the tip of my tongue to say: It all depends what you were doing in Glastonbury.

In a time of fresh breezes, with temperatures soaring into the high seventies, we took a picnic one day into Alexandra Park, and lay down in the long grass before the palace, the scaffolding still up before the View Bar, as it had been for fifteen years, and a fellow in blue overalls who appeared to be brushing the stone lion's mane, combing it out, as you sank into the long grass. Before us the greyness and high-rise blocks and gasometers and glass, the city was laid out.

'If you took out the plug it would all flow down the sink,' you said. 'Oh God am I *tired*! I could sleep for a week.'

'Where are you working now?'

'For your bunch.'

'Who they?'

'The Irish Tourist Board in New Bond Street.' You didn't hit it off with the boss nor the 'snooty' lady assistants, but you liked Ned the doorman who liked Jameson.

So I was waiting for you there, walking about Cork Street

and into New Bond Street and seeing through plate glass the stuck-up bitches stalking about on their high heels, talking to customers and smiling their brittle smiles, and saw an old love passing by. Petra grown old with all her charms quite gone passed me by twice, window-shopping. A midget looked up smiling into my face.

'We don't have no Underwoods here,' Ned the Irish doorman said stoutly. 'None by the name of Sally neither.'

A taxi drew up at the kerbside and you stepped out, miming amazement to see me there.

'Madame Lauriol de Barney, I presume?'

'None other.'

Ned escorted you up the steps as if you were royalty. A pair of Mohawks were passing in bovver boots and one called up after you *'Gizzakiss!'*

Flynn the drug-pusher and pimp who had young Irish girls on the game as soon as they came over from Ireland had brazenly suggested marriage to you, hinting at a settlement, and was prepared to drop his Swedish girlfriend. Flynn was from Limerick and never removed his brown snap-brim fedora.

Your moods were up and down now; oftener down than up.

'And what of that?'

For us all the graces of courtship were wanting, those nice preliminaries to intimacy, then intimacy itself, based on mutual trust and attraction, 'the charming variations': the bottle of Jameson on the table, avocados and Muscadet in the fridge, fresh sheets turned back, a window thrown open upon a place I had never been, possibly Middle Chinnock. The first sallies of passion in a village in south Somerset.

Spasms of furious lubricity were not 'on' at Grand Avenue on Sunday afternoons, in what Germans call 'the little shepherd hour', given the frosty manner that Beamish our host had seen fit to adopt towards you. Lethal Silver Bullets were still being prepared in the kitchen by the lord and master of the manse, while Riley groaned and slobbered, licking a cone-shaped prick red as a tulip damp with the morning's dew. But Beamish's heart was not in it, and a

Mickey Finn or cyanide were uppermost in his thoughts, not stiff cocktails.

'The hunched vulture on its reeking branch,' I said. Beamish had a clever way of getting your dander up, opening wide his ale-coloured calculating eyes, letting you run on, getting you riled. Then he would cut in: 'Don't *shout* at me, Sally. You're shouting again.' Then you would fly off the handle, as he knew you would.

We sat on a public bench in Cherry Tree Park in East Finchley and saw the tube trains come and go overground and spread the good Italian cheese (Pon) you had found on baguettes bought from an Indian shop, and over us the span of leafless branches, with some crows, one of which shat copiously and accurately.

'Even the crows despise us,' you said.

'Why does the name Manzoni remind me of some soft Italian cheese?'

We discussed our future: we had none. About us lay the miasmic and spirit-ridden forest, groans of animal resignation leaking from it. Your jealousy had become fertile in its inventiveness. We had nowhere to go.

We lived in an area where marriages broke up. Couples were living with different partners, or were letting rooms, or pimping on the sly, or had moved away, the children suffering. Buzz had left her computer husband Alex, as had Molly Gentle her Devon farmer, as had the rabid and redheaded Beth Brocklehurst ('Mrs Bracegirdle') her Jewish dentist in Golders Green, as had Eunice the Nudist her publisher husband. About us had begun to form what English brewers call a 'chill haze', having something critical to do with false fermentation.

You were browned off; things were looking a bit dodgy. Meaning that more unpleasant experiences were yet in store. 'The amazed hushed burning of hope and dream two-and-two engendered,' as Mr Faulkner had most intemperately phrased it, would not be for us. We were the twin miseries from Grimm: Joringel and Jorinde dressed in black velvet, holding hands, gazing sorrowfully into each other's eyes. Or the feverish saints John and Theresa clinging to the bars to prevent themselves levitating; for to be permanently earthbound can be anathema to some stricken souls.

Sexual love is a form of madness. ('I'm mad about you!' cries the besotted party. 'I'd drink your piss! I'm mad for it!') There is of course the well-known element of pursuit in sexual relationships, but with us it was carried to extremes; it was all flight and pursuit.

You discovered my *destino* in Buzz's tarot pack at her long refectory table. It said: 'Meeting the Lord in a narrow street; one sees the Wagon dragged back, the Oxen halted, a man's hair and nose cut off.'

Buzz was quite silent for a change, looking from one to the other, mystified.

To walk by a winding tributary, one of the winding tributaries of the Avon, not Ebble nor Nadder nor the Wylye, but the Marden that flows through Wiltshire, enclosed as it is permanently by Gloucestershire, Dorsetshire, Somerset, Berkshire and a part of Hampshire; ever renowned for the splendour of its country seats ('passing pleasant and delight-some', Camden thought), and to come to the heron's careful tread in the mud

and arrive at close of day at a whitewashed cottage, the same mentioned once in the Domesday Book, to a long deal table for working at and eating from, a bedroom with a double bed by a window, always left open; to be under the same roof together, in the same bed at night, where we ought to be.

Nothing is ever left anywhere but in the mind; imper-manence is the true state of nature, deterioration and decay of the human husks. We had to all intents and purposes stopped living. Love would be a burying of the other deep within oneself. And I would take you in with all your dark

167

moods, your insecurity; mutual trust would have the
security and permanence of the grave. Since I wouldn't be
with you, nor see you, you would not age but would stay the
same forever: always thirty-nine. Absence fixes attention to
these static moments (the centrefold model girl in panties on
the kitchen table), all that memory (or longing) can fix
upon. You there then doing that. There would be more and
more of the talk and less and less of the reality to record, until
in due course (as with a prisoner doing life), as the reality
fades, so too the recounting of it; until only jibberish
remains. A fellow attempting to erase his features with his
own free hand. We shall have to watch out, shan't we?

The car drew up alongside me opposite the Whittington
Hospital at Archway and the driver rolled down his window
and politely inquired of the road to Dover, he was heading
for the Dover ferry. I started to give elaborate and imprecise
instructions but stopped to say if he could give me a lift to
Islington or The Angel I would set him directly on his way.
He said he was a little strapped for time but of course he
would oblige. The transistor was playing in a muted fashion,
Bryan Ferry singing 'These Foolish Things'. He said he was in
the British army stationed in Germany and was going back
on leave. I put him on the right road. At least I hope so.
    Bullock, Proctor, Lightburn, Gutteridge and Lees-Milne
were ho-ho-hoing away like foghorns by the service hatch;
saloon bar swells trying to outsmart each other, Graham,
Howard, Mark Sylvester and Anthony. 'More ale here,
landlord!' thundered Graham Bullock, pounding the
wooden counter with his pewter mug. Proctor and the
belligerent Lightburn were loudly calling for more brandy
and pink gins, all in their proper places.
    'There's less in this than meets the eye!' Oh, ho, ho, ho,
ho! went the foghorns. Tremlett hovering about as usual,
Gussy Towell staring out the window at the clouds.
    'Are you leaving us in a marked manner?'

Every Tuesday night The Prince was thronged for jazz. The
Tuesday night crowd would turn up: Howard and Elsa, Nick

Ridley of manslaughter fame and his hangers-on, Darcy Brewster who had a coffee-house near The Gate House, Eoin Belton (O.C.) and the lovely Geraldine Quinn, Willie Edgecumbe the old queen who had kept his queerness secret through forty years of marriage, and drank whiskey on his doctor's orders 'because it eased the strain on his heart'. Willie Moulton the quiet accountant (an alcoholic despite outward rectitude, concealing extensive consumption of Stag and J & B by cashing large cheques several times weekly in the butcher's shop opposite the Prince, admitting to the largest meat bill in north London), tormented Angela Harris the vibraphone player, Freddy Byswater and his dark friend Lincoln the flautist who was very slowly consuming halves of draught Guinness with an abstracted aristocratic manner, befitting a great lord or a Persian cat. Freddy himself, the true Scouse, drunk as a skunk and twice as sly. Our Maudie the eighty-year-old retired nurse who lived in one of the almshouses behind Highgate School. Christine the opera-singer, an imbiber of sweet cider. Russell the accountant and Jeff the gardener, the Camden controller of plants, looking like a Guards officer and much given to rolling silences. Lady Vi ('Bitter Veronica') the Scots witch of coven fame.

Wally Fawkes played alto sax with his Welsh pianist Bleddyn wallowing in Methodist guilt. Wally had played with Sidney Bechet in Paris and could still blow a relaxed alto sax – Strayhorn's 'Take The A Train', Hodges' 'That's The Blues, Old Man', or his own bitter-sweet rendering of 'Autumn In Tufnell Park'. He drank little while playing, halves of Yorkshire bitter and the occasional Scotch. Liked more Scotch whilst chewing the fat with his admirers, and a large one on leaving.

I went there on Tuesdays. I had known The Prince under four different managements, when Saloon and Public parts were divided by partition, before the wooden floor was laid. But you had known it in the times of the Compton brothers. You never went there on Tuesday nights.

Lincoln was smiling into his Guinness in an ecstasy of dark contemplation and Freddy (like some villain in a Graham Greene 'entertainment') pushed himself up close to me and said out of the corner of his mouth: 'Seen anything of our Sally lately?'

As you were rarely to be seen, I moved away from those haunts into other haunts, drank half pints of Sam Smith's old-brewed English bitter at The Bakery Oven in Paddington where the two Italian owners were playing childish video games of Formula One with the racing cars running off the track and crashing, the Italians crying out 'I don't get no keeks aghta pro soccer.' Or drinking frothy pints of Directors' with Swainson at The Star and Garter in Poland Street near his office in Noel Street, Soho.

'That was Olivier in a Panther stuck in a traffic jam,' said a regular upon entering.

'Is that geezer gone then?'

Different tribes frequented these parts, speaking a different argot. Muswell Hill was neither in the city nor in the country, but an interim place, on the way to Potters Bar ('Are you stuck for a bit of cement?'). Arabs in flowing robes stood on their balconies outside top-storey apartments overlooking the cricket ground, breathing in the polluted London air, rich as Croesus.

One chilly grey day towards the end of May, following one of fourteen hours' sunshine, the sky teeming with swifts returned from Africa, you came up the hill past The Green Man, dressed that day in weed-grey battle-fatiques with engineer's pockets let into the thigh, dressed to kill. First I had seen your face, *'mit allen Wassern gewaschen'*, as the Germans say, then your shoulders, then your hips and the rest of you, a ravaged face coming up the hill. You had 'wept buckets', because of me.

You had cried out in your sleep, waking Moose; and naturally that had once more aroused his suspicions. *The heart tormented and buried with no further guarantee of success or performance.*

'Ever abstained for any length of time from the carnal act?' I asked Margaret.

She attended her Octogenarian Lover on Wednesdays as

regular as the four seasons passing or the seven cycles of change, sometimes letting herself in very quietly with the milk on Thursday mornings, before her bath and breakfast, and then departing to work in Kentish Town, pussyfooting out.

'No. Why? Have you?'

'Certainly,' I said.

'For how long?'

'Oh, two and a half years, once.'

Margaret gave me a deliberating look and crossed her long stylish legs.

'What are you looking at? Me or something behind me?' I asked.

'I'm looking at you,' Margaret said. 'It's a wonder it's not sticking out of your ears.'

Now she was preparing to leave the room.

'I would assume that you're still quite attractive to women,' was her parting shot.

'Shall we chance another Silver Bullet? What do you think? Would it be wise, so early in the day? What do you say?' Beamish inquired silkily.

'Excellent sack,' I said, 'let's give it a whirl.'

Beamish gave me a look under lowered lids and went into the kitchen to assemble the powerful ingredients. He sometimes gave the impression that even his eyelashes were freckled, which would naturally be impossible, but it would not have been the only impossible thing about this Duke of Guise.

The thriller had been rejected by two publishers. When the first rejected it, he kept this quiet from Mitzi, and said he was changing publishers. After more rejections he would begin researching his book on gold. Mitzi swallowed it all.

His former employers, who had made him redundant (or sacked him), sent a man round for the company car. Shortly before he released it he was charged with drunken driving. At the station he was offered a *Mirror* to read but refused to read it, demanded *The Times*. 'Oh so we are going to be like that?' the copper said, and led him to a cell to sober up.

On his release next morning bright and early he took a taxi to the Dorchester and breakfasted royally there. You get the best breakfast in London at the Dorchester.

One day in The Prince I chanced to fall into conversation with Shorland-Ball, DSO, whom Beamish had wickedly nicknamed Biggles, and he told me he had flown in Beaufighters at night during the London Blitz, and been awarded a 'gong' – self-deprecating, the gong was the DSO.

Anyway he and some brother officers were summoned to Buckingham Palace to receive their medals from the hand of King George VI. They had had a few vodkas in the Ritz to calm their nerves, climbed into a taxi and said 'To the Palace!' But they were no sooner into the reception line than all four of them wanted a leak. Biggles had a word with the major-domo. 'Impossible, gentlemen,' he said, 'that's quite impossible.' The King was expected any minute, and in any event the palace had no public toilets. They would just have to grin and bear it, the major-domo said.

Now they were in a fix. Biggles drew aside the velvet drapes of a tall window and they got into the embrasure, opening the window a foot or two. Then in turn all four of them pissed out onto the King's flowerbeds below. In great acrobatic arcs no doubt, all four being superb flyers. Biggles, the captain, went last. He began to piss and seemed to hear a great crowd cheering, and looking out, member in hand, whom did he see just leaving the forecourt in an open carriage but the old ex-Queen Mary in her tiara. As the stately carriage drawn by spanking greys swept out by the open palace gates she raised up her bright parasol, and bells rang out all over London town.

5
Ye Loste Lande (London Zoo)

Your dream: a large black limousine awaits outside the library. My seat slides back. You slip behind the wheel and touch a button. As we drive off a portable bar opens out and on the muted stereo Bryan Ferry begins 'These Foolish Things'. We swing away to the dream cottage called 'Bullsease' or 'La Casa Maganaria', far from London, in the depths of the country.

As I help myself to a gin and tonic with ice-cubes and a slice of lemon you reach back with a good cigar. Trumpets are thrust from under clouds as we roll along. Piercing silvery music accompanies us as we pass through the Vale of Kennet in Berkshire. A signpost points towards Pangbourne and Goring. We travel grandly on, you at the wheel.

'Bullsease' is all prepared. You show me the long working table, the anglepoise, a window overlooking rolling countryside without any pylons. I smell roasting rabbit. In an old beamed bedroom the trusty fourposter stands by an open window. Once more we take passage into the realm of transparent bliss.

Framed daguerreotypes of Schumann and Wagner hang on either side of the fourposter, a wood fire burns in the grate, and the faces of cats are pressed to the window; the garden giving its last show in the evening light.

Neptune and Jupiter are now about to make their presence felt in a rather spectacular way. We are naked as salmon between the blue sheets that smell freshly of rosemary. 'There is no "Thou shalt not",' you say.

It was one of those evenings when all the bars of Highgate

seemed packed with braying idiots and Beamish and I had decided to move back up the hill.

'The deepest despair is full of secret satisfactions,' I said. 'Learning comes with suffering – or so the old Greeks believed. In twenty years or so of tenure the headmaster of Eton flogged an average of ten boys a day, beating Latin and Greek into their bums.'

'No finer example of emollient irony.'

We were at the 134 bus stop opposite The Woodman. Two slutty female punkers got up as Gestapo officers with studs in black leather and glittering accessories of bottle-caps and militant insignia stood waiting, a little apart. A pantechnicon passed, the driver in his high cabin offering them a stiff-arm Nazi salute.

'Silly bugger,' said the thinner one, wispy hair dyed purple under a headpiece set at a jaunty angle.

'Sod the fukkah,' said her stout friend.

Two double-deckers rounded the corner, bound for the Broadway.

'Up or down?' asked Beamish as he swung adroitly aboard.

'Up with you.'

We ascended into thick tobacco fumes on the upper deck. A little crabby man with afflicted eyes and protruding ears came and sat behind us, wheezing.

'In the seventeenth century, if men wanted to smoke,' I said, 'they were put out of doors by their womenfolk.'

Presently the church of St James hove to on our right and we descended to find the punkers effing and blinding on the platform and who but Terence de Vere White walking by with some shopping in a plastic bag. We walked by the Muswell Hill Bookshop and entered the back or public bar of The Baird where a foul-mouthed Scot was holding the floor.

'What will you have?' asked Beamish.

Mitzi told us how she came through a hole in the hedge, in her pyjamas, and was standing in her bare feet at the front door with the key turning in the lock when she heard a familiar breezy male American voice say 'Hi there, Mitzi,

174

how about a quickie?' She waved at him. 'A blow-job then?'
She pushed open the door. 'What about a hand-job?' the
American persisted. The door was closing and Mitzi heard 'I
suppose a ride would be out of the question?' And then the
roar: 'Goddammit Mitzi, how about a rump-roast?' It was in
the early hours of the morning.

Chance would be a fine thing. What was happening? Who
was losing? Mitzi was playing The Tough Cookie, 'Dirty
Gerty' or Matilda Makejoy. For six months she had had an
affair with Moose when you were in hospital with a bad
back; Beamish in those days being still married to Gerda the
Norwegian, who could freeze a room at will by entering it,
prior to their separation.

Riley was stretched out at our feet like a hound after the
hunt. And then curled up with his nose into his anus,
twitching and dreaming of the chase, whimpering, then a
lingering breaking of wind.

'Manners,' said Mitzi mildly.

'This morning in Euston Station I felt I was in Hell,'
Beamish said, prodding Riley with his toe. 'Mush, Riley,
mush! Comb the woods.'

Riley in his slumber heaved a heavy sigh.

'Ever been to the Felix au Port in Antibes? No? Graham
Greene dines there. And in Rule's, I'm told, with his brother.
Shall we have another Silver Bullet?'

'Let's go to the Alex,' Mitzi said. 'Riley could do with an
outing.'

So the four of us, three not sober, set out for The
Alexandra. Riley licked his master's hands as he was leashed
and dragged Beamish over the threshold with the force of a
thunderbolt as soon as the door opened.

'Lead on, oh great sniffer-hound,' cried Mitzi, who did
enjoy outings to licensed premises.

Small twittery birds still invisible in their roosting places had
begun stirring and twittering preparatory to yet another
aubade as we stepped onto the wrought-iron balcony above
the fire-escape and felt the air and saw London below us in
the morning haze, the sight-screens on Crouch End

playing-fields and the distant silhouette of St Paul's over the river.

'Don't know how I'll get out of this one,' you said, looking up from the second step at me in dressing-gown and slippers, covering my hand with your warm hand.

'I'll have to find a pond.'

You looked down at the two sad sycamores growing together with their roots gone into the foundations of the garage next door, their fates sealed already.

'Poor things, they're dying for water.'

You began to descend the spiral fire-escape.

'Go back to bed. Or have a bath.'

In The Whittington and Cat above Archway a bored Irish labourer asked his friend: 'Djya know any new jokes?'

Their boots, caked with mud, rested on the rungs of two bar stools set side by side. Their bodies and minds were thick; all day long they had been working in London drains. The rough and ready friend stared bemusedly about the bar as if the missing jokes might be flying here and there, like bats; but he could see none. He shook his head, dipped his lips into black draught Guinness.

'I know horse-breeding inside out,' said his friend, and began to speak of the racing in Ireland. Of Leopardstown, Fairyhouse, the drenched Curragh.

The stout Irish publican was examining me from head to toe out of the corner of his eye. The place and company depressed me; it was another bar in rural Ireland with its regular retinue of malcontents drinking draught Guinness. I left and passing four or five pubs made my way to The Alexandra opposite the police station, where I found Jack Stack the Irish equestrian champion of the 1920s holding forth. Jack was flushed and talkative, wore a floppy hat, making forceful hand-signals, attempting to muscle his way into any conversation, any group buying drinks.

'Do you know I sang today like an Irish linnet!' Wally the collector of matchboxes sat crouched over his Campari and splash at the end of the bar where the young Mayoman stood with his pint of lager. The wild-eyed Mayoman was red in the face, dressed in his Mass-going serge suiting stiff as armour. His wife was with him; she could have been his mother, looking crushed and flustered like a hen.

'Are you stuck for a bit of cement?'

Wally looked around with a mild surmise and shook his head.

'Don't give a sod.'

'It's alright for some.'

'Tell me this,' the equestrian champ asked point blank, 'is your grandfather *still* alive?'

'God what drips!'

I finished my drink in a hurry and walked down to The Prince, where I ordered a White Shield from Trudy, said I would be back in a minute, and stepped into Barclays Bank two doors down, beyond the betting shop. A heavy butcher was leaning up against the counter in a striped apron smelling of blood, depositing bloodstained wads of notes secured with rubber bands. I stood behind him and tried not to breathe.

I changed some money and went back to find my drink poured out and Trudy warming her backside at one of the two coal fires.

'If you want anything just call.'

Trudy had a pleasant Scots accent. In the times when I did not see you, the name Glastonbury uttered in a bar, or the nerest suggestion of a Somerset burr, this name and these murmurous sounds were sufficient to fill me with an ineffable sadness. You brought to mind those suffering females in early French cinema, Arletty nude in a revolving tub of water, Lys like a stoat, Vivianne Romance naked under a fur coat, Michèle Morgan in a belted raincoat in *Quai des Brumes*, but closer still Madeleine Robinson as the maid in *Une Si Jolie Petite Plage* saving Gérard Philipe from suicide at the seaside in winter; those who willingly gave all for love and came to sticky ends themselves, shimmering naked in a lake: Hedy Lemarr in *Extase*. Such fitful gleams.

The Prince of Wales. The regulars were all there, standing or sitting in their accustomed places with their usual drinks, old

Maudie in her plant-pot hat (askew) drinking herself into oblivion from pension day (Thursday) to lunchtime on Sunday after church, when she began to run out of funds, persevering with light ale and whisky, sometimes peeing discreetly on the boarded floor.

There too would be Edgecumbe, Moulton and Gorst, Dobson and Squire Sprigge (a prat of the highest order), all admiring Annie the barmaid, known as the Barnsley Baby-snatcher, much fancied until huge increase in diameter of arse curbed their fancy. Christine the opera-singer (sweet cider), the Unknown Actor, starring in *Ronald Rat – the Series* as a character called Darcy de Farcy. Angela the vibraphone player. It was Saturday morning and they were all there, talking their heads off, and in the thick of them (unseen) Beamish!

'I happen to have this passion for penitential music,' the prissy voice said. 'Did you know that Tibetan monks sang in chords?'

'Right on, squire.'

'Sod the little so-and-so,' another voice said down the bar.

Through the hatch, under the line of up-ended wine-glasses above the serving area, on the far counter I saw the freckled hand of Beamish.

I drank my White Shield and withdrew discreetly by the back door, passing by the phone kiosks and the public conveniences for ladies and gents, and in by the side door of The Angel, where I ordered another White Shield.

The Bird in Hand, Friern Barnet. The smell of damp lengths of sawn wood came from the timberyard and a stout boozer in bargee's trousers with hair greased back under the snap-brim green pork-pie hat worn with some panache was pushing the door in to the stinks, upon cardiac cases with hairy chests playing darts, and a thick pall of Virginia tobacco smoke suggestive of stale collective farting. Then sluggish White Shields being set before us, no offer to pour them, a dull pain in the eyes. I approach crabwise, the only way I know, dragging you behind me. The regulars were gassing away in the fumes, as if inured to discomfort.

'Geezers wiff broken backs,' said a rough voice, 'an' broken necks an' birds wiff bleeden tits 'angen ahht.'

'Shut yoh bleeden cake'ole.'

'Sor*reee*.'

You are your most characteristic, sitting with bowed head at the end of the line of out-patients in the casualty ward of the Whittington Hospital. Then it was your turn. I held your hand. Not a murmur escaped you as the lady doctor threaded five slow stitches into your chin, even if the first stitch had followed hard upon the quick injection.

We waited at the bus stop. The injection and stitches were 'like a cold wind blowing off a snow mountain', you told me. 'It's like being dipped in silver.'

A number 134 rounded the corner and drew up before us.

'Nip on,' I said.

'My nipping on days are over.'

We took the left-hand front seats on the upper deck as the bus started up the hill.

'My face?'

'Still intact.'

'My arm?'

'I can feel it. Still there.'

'My leg?'

'Still on you.'

'Good.'

It was a Sunday in the early afternoon when you had phoned to say you were with Buzz and could I come over. I bought two litres of Italian wine and rolling tobacco and papers and walked across. You met me in shorts at the door, embraced me, led me to the bathroom where you dashed water on my face and neck, my hands. Buzz was in the garden with the children. We drank wine in the sun and Buzz dozed off in a deckchair and at an upper window next door a fellow preparing food in a T-shirt was very interested in your movements, now circling the flowerbeds on a child's bike, in shorts, with brown legs, smiling at me. Then you applied the brakes and went in slow motion over the handlebars as the bike reared up, and head first into the

179

stones of the rockery. You lay there stunned and pumping blood. The chin wound was deep. I helped you up, now pale and bleeding, hands and thighs covered in blood, and then you were throwing up into the begonia beds.

Buzz phoned your doctor but he was out. She drove us to the Whittington and waited in the Out-patients of the casualty wards. Dr Sue Ainsley said to come back in three days to have the stitches out. I said I would go with you.

Buzz said she had never seen anything like it. You preparing for a difficult delivery and the husband (Brian) holding your hand in the public ward.

'*Bee-bee!*' Buzz screeched, at her most Barbadan. She drove you home. You didn't want a drink.

As you went slowly over the handlebars you were smiling trustfully at me, and the fellow in the string vest was looking down in amazement, something burning on the pan, as you smashed head first into the sharp rocks.

Dr Hilary (out on a call) was another of your many admirers; something had gone on between you in Paris. Nava the Russian lady kept imploring you to join her in the sauna.

My earliest loves were your unknown rivals. You were most fertile in your jealousies; for it was not only jealousy but jealousy multiplying. The blonde with the ankle bracelet in the flower shop at Fortis Green across from The Alexandra; the bar girl with long hair at Athene's; the girl from Kent who cut my hair at Cut 'n' Dry near the off-licence, these were all said to be your 'rivals'. And before them, cohorts of unknown teasers; the sexy tax inspectress ('that little silky lady') being the latest in line. Ortega says that in loving we abandon the tranquillity and permanence within ourselves and virtually migrate towards the objects of our desire; this constant state of migration is what it is to be in love – a constant state of migration.

I waited for you in a heavy drizzle of rain, walking up and down outside Dirty Dick's on Tottenham Lane, with darkness falling and the rain pouring down. An absent-minded fellow with open umbrella brushed against one of two drenched black brothers, half turning and hostile.

'Wottcho fukken brolly, mite!'

The ancient Greeks before battle on the pass, combing out their tangled yellow hair. And then you came drifting, drenched, up the hill, and we passed into the warmth and din of Dirty Dick's.

'Was you a Navy man as well?' a red-faced man asked a broad bent back at the bar.

'Ah've 'ad a go at everting,' the broad back answers stoutly.

'Nigel, 'ave we got any barley wine?' one barman called out to another. They were running swiftly to and fro.

'What will you 'ave?' I said.

One fresh day we alighted from a number 134 in Camden Town by the public toilets there and The Mother Red Cap and solitary drunken Irish in a sorry state, and walked up the hill and paid out some money to be admitted through the turnstiles of the London Zoo.

In the apiary the caged ones stretched out their long arms and took flying leaps at the trapeze. They reached out slowly for the bars, lower jaw out, showing their teeth. Hurling hay about; one dark ape with a finger up his wide nostril. A small black monkey was using its finger to draw with its own excrement, like Genet in prison in *Notre Dame des Fleurs*. With languorous movements capuchins swung on the branches of rootless trees, moving about in the quasi-wilderness of the dungy cage, amid nuts, orange peel, a begging bowl, necessities for these 'lifers' perhaps born into captivity, ignorant of the great roaring jungle. Here all the ceremonies of an idle life.

We passed out of there and into the walled compound of the hippos. On the dusty back of one standing still below us I scratched our epigraph: B. AMAT S. *Können Tiere lügen*?

'Can animals lie?' I asked.

'Of course not, silly.'

The mighty she-baboon sat in straw. Her dry leathery paps, the tufted hair on the domed skull like fluff on a coconut, the deep-set eyes hidden and furtive in the concavity of their sockets, were things to behold. Above the troubled fuzzy eyebrows, those ridges, the corrugations of a narrow subhuman forehead were signalling God knows what itch, fury, perplexity, bafflement; twitchy and colicky, in slow motion in a softly mimed buffoonery. For here was a great creature who could kill with her embrace, had she a mind to kill.

One absented stubby finger probed up to the joint into one wide nostril; then followed a concentrated study of the findings, the snot studied, tasted with a flutter of blubbery lips, then swallowed. Quasimodo was leering, gone female, gone bananas; the she-beast oh so uniquely self-pervaded, existence behind bars forever, in a strange void. A coloured diagram on a reduced atlas showed where the species sprang from; and in another cage the gibbons were hooting and shrieking as if still in the rain forests of remote Borneo. The Madagascar vari (whose scream in the night is said to stop the heart, twice) held its grim silence, staring downwards.

After the apiary the aquarium. In the darkness the illuminated tanks glowed and huge-lunged turtles swam underwater as though flying through the air. And I thought (obscurely, in this happiness), with me walks part of Bideford, Barnstaple, Lundy Island lost in mist, Appledore, the Mendips, the Polden Hills and the Quantocks, as I walked with you, sweet Sally.

Your warm hand felt for mine, took it. We walked through a darkly illuminated place become 'Ye Loste Lande'.

6
Black Napoleon in Drag

Already before mid October it was cold. The attic received no sun. I stayed away. At night you coughed, were staying away from work, letting the deaf ones fend for themselves, once more feeling 'peculiar'. Love first, then *farmacia*.

And once more the air began to nip and bite. You spoke in a disparaging way of hairy male intelligence, but did not specify anyone in particular.

One day you came up Muswell Hill, dressed all in black Kerseymere like a crow but for the Russian calf boots of ox-red from Oxfam, the selfsame boots wherein you hid my passport photo, like a dagger for Moose. We turned into The Swiss Chalet.

You had an *Evening Standard* in your net bag. I asked you to look up their astrologer Walker. Walker wrote of Pisces: 'Sun entering birth-sign on the 19th. Leave behind all you know to be limiting and emotionally harmful. The way ahead clearly signposted. Avoid travel plans this weekend. Keep to the minimum. Avoid people and situations you know will make you nervous and insecure. A truly exciting phase lies ahead and you cannot be browbeaten or upset by anyone.'

These days in the middle of February had all the charm of extended daylight. The nights were foggy and freezing. You were being pursued by a barman from The Baird who wouldn't take no for an answer.

Emerging from Athene's one night we saw a black transvestite sprinting by in the rain and a while later came upon the same party waiting for a cruising taxi outside the church, and you spoke to him (or her). She responded in a deep bass voice, was gorgeous, was *it*, but dangerous; hot as hell in shoes with six-inch stiletto heels, the gloved hand in matching kid held a monogrammed pouch of soft red leather and a small red parasol that a geisha might own; flashing brilliant dentures.

'Call me Dolores, lika dey do in de storybooks!'

She sported a Napoleonic cocked hat and under it a shoulder-length blonde wig. A late bus came by and she sprang nimbly aboard, waved a pale palm at us from the swaying platform, laughing a high-pitched laugh, her eyes flashing. Wig and hat were now removed in one swift motion in order to make an obeisance from the stage, exposing a curly black head tufted and shorn like a ram. Soldier Othello, the wheeling stranger.

A black Napoleon in drag was being carried away in an empty bus bound for the terminus at London bridge, the compelling stranger bending low to wave us adieu as *he* was carried off the hill and down into the sinful city below.

I had stood before the canopied bed in Longwood House on St Helena, touched the stiff valance, the yellowed sheet's fringe rigid as the collar about a dead neck, the bed itself reduced to the dimensions of a child's cot and in the billiard room below saw the cracked billiard balls on mildewed green baize now gone the bleached colour of grass in Sudan sun, the balls still in position haphazardly arranged about the baize, long-lost cannon shots and kisses, and one yellow cue laid down, as though no other hand had touched it since.

I thought of the unimaginably small determined body out of whom the will had been removed by death, a peaceful death-bed for one responsible for so much wholesale slaughter; the corpse still shrinking and now gone the dull green of *haricots verts* in the century and a half spent within the mouldering wood, the lead, the marble, in the monstrous sarcophagus on the Seine, the tomb much photographed by Japanese tourists all the year round, and every year round.

The same wary assured Corsican fixing the buttons of his tight waistcoat while critically examining his tongue (*le foie!*

in the convex mirror in the hall was keeping tabs on the gallant English sentries marching on and off duty outside; he was still the good soldier, stout and perspiring, spying on them through a spy-hole bored into the woodwork, going down to dine, his heart not in it. Walking over the field of Eylau where near 30,000 dead lay scattered, an open-air abattoir with many wounded, he turned one corpse over with the toe of his polished boot, and merely observed '*De la petite monnaie.*'

We were love's small change.

Heine had seen Bonaparte in his green uniform and little world-renowned cocked hat inverted like a calming compress upon that fertile and boiling Corsican brain of his, when he sat like marble astride his high horse, one marble hand lazily stroking the neck and mane; the emperor's hand and face had the hue which can be seen in Greek and roman busts. Heine remarked upon this, for he (of all people) had admired Napoleon, as had Chateaubriand and Beyle.

Bonaparte sat sombrely astride La Flamme de Temps out of Ancienne Flamme by Fils de Vesuvius, bred of the great mare Cabine Incendie by the legendary Volcan.

On Borodino field 75,000 had perished in one day, soiling their spotless breeches, some departing heavenward in fragmented form to face their Maker. Perhaps not even Napoleon himself could stomach it to walk amid that stench of carnage, his face gone chalk-white, the smell of freshly killed soldiers an aphrodisiac.

Dancer dear, the mummies of your crushed passions breathe upon me their irredeemable poison! Hot in pursuit of you were as motley a crew as might assemble in one dirty bar. Flynn the Pimp, Freddy the Fink, Harvey Wallbanger, the Fool on the Hill, the Rum Cove, the Bloke in the Blazer, the Horny Greek, the Baird Barman, the Right Prick, the Froglike Man in the Boat, to mention but these.

Riley seems a bit down in the mouth this morning,' I said. 'What ails him? Not getting his oats?'

'Never again,' Beamish said. 'Poor Riley had his

progenitive parts fixed by Mickey the Vet yesterday. He's got every reason for feeling poorly.'

'Poor Riley,' said I, patting the noble head, and was licked on the hand. 'Great sniffer dog, great putative father, alas!'

'What about a swift Silver Bullet?'

'Couldn't do us any harm,' I said.

'Oh, I'm not so sure about *that*,' beamed Beamish as he moved into the kitchen and began to prepare the lethal cocktails, humming. A number of cats outside the windows watched his every move. Murphy and Molloy and two others whose names I could not remember; Beamish called them Mitzi's children.

A sight as sad as sad can be: the garden giving its last show in the evening light and faces of cats pressed to the window. Permanence has forsaken our world and jeopardy taken its place. Age does us no favours. The past itself is probably the most potent and enduring of all known aphrodisiacs.

You had confessed that you had 'had it off' with someone I knew. I had suggested a number of names but it was not one of them, it was 'someone you know'. Pimping Flynn? Freddy Byswater? Alec the Copper? And, Stavros of all people, in a semi-rape upstairs in his premises, while you were waiting for me and I didn't come. And for all I know the nameless punker with the prick the size of a French *boulette* observed covertly in his crutch, 'under wraps'; he too perhaps had carnal knowledge of you.

'Your cock,' you said sadly. As if speaking of some wretched farmyard full of muck and feathers and the depressing odour of wet fowl; and over in one corner, under a dripping pear tree, a dishevelled brown hen being trodden into the earth by the swelling cock, in the teeming rain.

7
Battle of Hastings

Charing Cross station exists no longer. At Embankment a recorded male voice hollowly intoned 'Mind the gap!' over and over. And then I was away. An hour too early, missing you again, seeing love-bowers below, rolling cornfields of Sussex, stands of beech buffeted by the breeze, ferny gripes.

Sitting in the tube train coming down from Finsbury Park I was admiring the new murals in Charing Cross station and was carried on to Embankment and had to take a north-bound connection back, but still found myself too early in Euston. As a train for Battle was just leaving I took it, and it pulled away at 8.35 a.m.

'This is your God speaking,' an indistinct male voice boomed over the Inter-City tannoy system. The accent was distinctly working-class but from no known region. 'You are on the 8.35 train for Battle. If any passengers do *not* wish to go to Battle, it's too late now.'

God, and an English God at that, had a sense of humour. We hurtled on towards Battle.

Soon the sweet air of Sussex came through the open window, an odour of cut hay. Sussex was some eighty miles across, and I was travelling on into sunny countryside, by Hither Green, Petts Wood, under the immense strato-cumulus over the Weald, by Wadhurst and a fat smiling girl on a fat piebald pony following a pretty black-haired friend on a sorrel, off for a day's trekking. Stonegate ('England, Home and Beauty'), Etchingham, a heron flying over the stubble-fields, and what I took to be the ghost of Douglas Bader, the air ace, stumping heavily up and down Tonbridge station, waiting for the London train.

187

Cut wheatfields around Frant. Then Tunbridge Wells Central, the inevitable pottery, Sevenoaks. I counted only seven cabbage whites along the woody railway embankments between Petts Wood (lacking a possessive) and Battle. Pesticides destroy the butterflies, our world.

Then High Brooms, Grove Junction, Robertsbridge, and Brownies embarking at Battle station for a day's outing to Hastings. A damp mess of used clothes thrown out under a tree near a caravan site at the end of the road leading to the station; the balmy air of High Street. I walked over the famous battlefield with Professor Burns, felt nothing much; history's pomps are toy-like.

A Mexican couple were studying the battle array mounted in a glass case; toy lead soldiers on a field of green, an arrow in King Harold's eye.

'Look up in the sky, Hal, and tell me what you see.'

'I see the moon.'

'Well, how much farther do you want to see?'

The attack had been made uphill, great foolishness, over undulating terrain. The hidden bowmen, releasing their flights from a distance, killed at will. Modern warfare as such had begun – odd that the phlegmatic and peace-loving English should have invented it. The armoured knights attacked splendidly uphill with battleaxes raised, leaving behind them only a pond of blood. The battle area was smaller than expected; as Lord Byron, riding over it, had remarked upon the smallness of the field of Waterloo. Great deeds, as murder, require little space. To kill a man there is required a bright, shining and clear light. No sooner had a blood-red sun set behind the hazy border hills of Sussex than a paper-thin, bone-white sickle moon appeared in the sky, shrouded in cloud, to shine obliquely down on disordered and ghostly battle-dead at Hastings.

Overhead, orbiting in space, fixed upon an undeviating course, a trajectory of aligned accuracy that had not changed since observed in 87 BC by the seventeen-year-old stripling Caius Julius – in a time that went backwards – Halley's Comet had come around again, dragging a tail of luminous

gas said to be a hundred million kilometers long; a monster
of antiquity breeding in the upper air.

Ahead, unknown to Caesar, were the years on horseback,
sanguinary campaigns, promotion, war in Gaul. Not to
mention the Rubicon, the Ides of March, and a text to
trouble future generations of inkstained schoolboys baffled
by *De Bello Gallico*.

Orbiting overhead, letting off steam, the *rara avis* went
rocketing onward, dropping off gross tonnage of itself in its
haste to get beyond the sun. Nothing would be clear from
the crib, except gleams of half-extinguished light, diffuse
illusions; increasing and decreasing, no sooner seen than
gone. This manifestation not to be seen again by human eye
for seventy-six years, our lifespan, passing by without
leaving a trace – heaven's gas, numinous rejectamenta, a
will-o'-the-wisp in the night sky.

Jupiter's red spot indicates where it has been raining, not
bleeding, non-stop for seven hundred years. There is always
a sign, if you look for it. But William Duke of Normandy was
ignorant of all this as he dined with his army chiefs.

Celibate as an Abelite or the albatross that mates every
three years – chastity springing from lack of choice and a
fastidious mood (abstinence, as absence, makes the heart
grow less fond, *au fond*, makes it weary, also distorts the
reality of the absent one); and I'd been eighteen months in
that sorry condition when I first set eyes on you. The range
of the squonk is limited.

How came you in these parts? Where were you bred? To
escape into nothingness, struggle upward out of the
Nothing, struggle on. Expect few favours; we live in modern
times, after all. Sometimes you got tight by evening. One day
we had thirty-two 'jars' in The Nightingale, beginning with
Bloody Mary and ending with bitter. All your projects were
to come to nothing. Working for the Irish Tourist Board, for
the deaf, designing sandals, sculpting, making paper funeral
flowers for an undertaker; nothing came of all this. Another
life was pacing alongside your own.

Then you were in Somerset when your mother was dying

of cancer. You feared to stay in the house with your father. You said: 'I can't stand it.'

'We must have a child.' We'd call it Jarleth. You had such sweet fancies.

At first I couldn't even remember your name. Not even that most primitive courtesy. It was an odd name with a bucolic ring to it: Fairfax, Fielding, Rutland, Greenwood, Moormist, Mildwater, Thorneycroft, Atwood, Woodfall, Honeycombe, Summerbee, Oldfield, Loveridge. *Liebe*, Lord, how does that come in! Love, an accomplice between two ailing beings. Why, one must fear even to be *liked*.

We lived high up in the dim attic as man and wife, in a bedroom permeated with old sorrows. You dragged yourself out of bed and went to work in Gower Street, got up in fatigues and battle-dress, never a skirt, having some notion about your legs. In fact you had a very nice pair, for had you not danced on a table in The Prince of Wales with Dr Graham Chapman, later to become famous as one of the Monty Python jokers?

Your rig-out might be a mixture of English Lesbos and Italian *partigiani*: savanna boots, shore kit, jungle casual wear. You liked to garb yourself in the colours of autumn and winter, though I always associated you with summer and the things of summer. If summers would ever be like summer again, in England, they would be linked with you under the beech tree in Hadley Wood, dressed in savanna boots and earrings. Or in the reedy riverbed at Brickendon Green, with nothing on at all.

We were together on the Spice Islands, on Fisherman's Wharf, on Banana Bay, on the nudist beach called Saline on St Barthelemys, when we were alone in Buzz's flat in Coniston Road with the louvred blinds half closed and the light out and you came naked from the bathroom. Buzz had framed and hung up bright coloured materials cut in shapes of Caribbean things to make a sort of stitched collage, and naked on the sofa we might just as well have been under waving palms.

The massive brown prize bull 'Hang-Down' stood masterfully among the fidgety heifers, his seraglio, steamily breathing out from his grass-packed stomach where the mighty parts hung below, his breeding equipment. One of the heifers began scratching its throat on the top bar of the gate, rolling her cowy eyes, presenting dungy hindquarters – what Dean Swift called 'the dishonourable parts' – to her lord and master, the same parts beclotted with much-sat-in shit to which moss and weeds and whortleberries had affixed themselves. The rest of the herd were restless and irritable. Above the gate a crudely hand-writ sign on a piece of board nailed to a tree announced

FERITS FOR SALE

'Hang-Down' lumbered slowly and grandly through his anxious herd, the ring in the wet nose suggesting wickedness, the russet hump of muscle in the ridged tight-packed testes proof positive of exceptional bully virility; confirmed a moment later, if proof were needed, when, exposing a pizzle the length of a bicycle pump but of the diameter of a good-sized cucumber, the great beast attempted to mount the five-bar gate.

You backed off, perhaps finding this as alarming as the free-and-easy antics of the belly-dancer in Stavros's cellar amid the sweating Greeks.

It was Sunday and we had come by train from Finsbury Park (no sign of Moose on the platform or prowling the waiting-room, and thereabouts I felt most uneasy, for you walking there would lead him to me), travelling out into the country to Brickendon Green and into The Ploughboy just in time to hear the suddenly very active barman calling out Time, *please*, gents!' and see the regulars straggling out.

Twice in the dry riverbed, once in the wood, with sunlight pouring across a field, and opening-time come around again, was not Brickendon Green a veritable *Garten der Lüste*?

In the ferny gripe you lay nude with an incandescent amber glow, axillary tufts drenched, pussy sopping, lips moistful, for me: I knew you again. You gave yourself to me. You were my Amaryllis. Then I kissed you avidly all over.

'Having kissed you avidly all over,' I said, 'I must drink your piss.'

191

You said nothing, looked at your watch, smiled.

'Would a pint of Director's not do?'

We dressed, combed ourselves out, and were among the first into the reopened Ploughboy, as five hours before we had been among the last out. The interval whiled away like Adam and Eve without shame under a spreading beech, walking by the wheatfield and the green, marvelling at the parts of 'Hang-Down'.

Weakened and dehydrated by long bouts of kissing I ordered up pints and halves of foaming Director's and turkey breasts with good fresh bread, with which you wanted pickles. *Pickles!* I never knew where I was with you. You told me that you had seen a pencilled invitation in the public toilet in Fortis Green, asking for beaver shots.

'What are they?'

You told me. You said I was a badger, my youngest son a fox. You had felt yourself under observation on the Broadway and looking across the road saw Shangar watching, still as a fox. You had stared at him, and he at you; looking away you looked back, and he had vanished, fox-like, melted away. You rarely went onto the Broadway. You spoke again of your old man and his carryings-on; old Nutt sounded like old Karamazov. Paedophilia and incest were on the increase. 'I won't play games,' you said. Was it a threat or a promise?

I was a badger, my youngest lad a fox, a woman in Fortis Green wanted beaver shots. And you liked the voice of Elkie Brooks, Bryan Ferry singing 'These Foolish Things', the Aloha Boys belting out 'Only You'. Buzz's white portable throbbed, we danced across the sanded floor, the three small Deerings already at our private parts, poking and sniggering.

We drank White Shields in Harry's Bar in Hampstead near the ponds. The river flooded the valley and the sea came in, while Wells Choir sang Vivaldi's *Gloria* as if Cromwell's hangman had never strung up the abbot. Our maternal grandmothers had the same Christian name: Lily. We were both Pisceans. The double of John Arlott drank Guinness in The Shepherds on Archway Road and you told me how as a young girl you had offered to go to bed with an English wicket-keeper in a hotel in Derby. The place was marbled. You wore your mother's dress, your hair up bouffant-style; virginity had become a burden. Then champagne was ordered and you let your hair down. You made it quite clear to the handsome wicket-keeper that virginity was a burden to you. He said 'You are too nice for this,' and sent you home in a taxi.

Then we were in The Shepherds and it was near Christmas and you came in and began reading my copy of the *New Statesman*. I saw across from you seated by the gas fire a middle-aged florid Tory gent reading his *Evening Standard* and to hand a pint of Guinness on an oval table.

'It's Denis Compton,' I said. You looked across at him.

'More like John Arlott.'

This strange hybrid, the Dashing Cavalier, the witty cricket commentator, seemed immune to his present surroundings, not lifting his eyes, reading the sports page. Contradictions *abounded*.

Mike the barman at The Alex had not always been the Leviathan he was; once he had been a pacy medium-pacer knocking down wickets. Now he was a Mack Sennett heavy, polishing a glass, one watery bloodshot eye fixed amicably on me.

'Where's the lovely lady?'

We drank foaming pints at Ye Olde Monken Holt and rode on the top deck of the Barnet bus with foul-mouthed and aggressive Mohawks out for an night of booze-up and wog-bashing in dirty Leicester Square; when not frequenting The Prince of Wales, The Gate House or The Rose and Crown or The Duke of Norfolk in Highgate Village. Sometimes for a change of atmosphere we visited The Flask or The Wrestlers, The Red Lion and Sun, The Victoria or The Bull, The Clissold Arms, that morgue, or two Irish pubs on the Archway Road called The Shepherds, The Whittington and Cat, both patronized by labouring Irish, sitting on high bar stools drinking Guinness, all ears, like bad spuds.

At Oscar's, The Green Man and The John Baird we were known. A morning of Bloody Marys down at The Royal Oak might be followed by an evening of White Shields at The Alex, or down in Dirty Dick's bar on the Tottenham Lane, or over at Bad Bob's in East Finchley. We passed by The Bull and Gate, The Drum and Monkey, The Tally Ho sans exclamation mark, avoiding the meat-heads in The Mother Red Cap in grimy Camden Town. Thrice you abandoned me outside Chicago 20, wept, said it was all over, fled down the hill into the dark of Crouch End. I never knew where you lived; down there somewhere.

One morning in The Prince I spoke to Mick Minogue, late of Scariff in the County Clare. He told me he was doing a job in Cromwell's old town house in Pond Square across the way, and praised the ornate woodwork. His mother had called him from the Beyond. Mick had heard her distinctly the old thin voice of his mammy, and his hair stood on end He sat down and drank a bottle of Scotch 'as if it were water'.

He had a hot tip for White City that evening, the dog track so we moved to the betting shop next door. The crabbed finger went down the list of runners, Mystical Hound and Peaceful Rouge were fancied.

And in you came, blown in by the morning, breathless.

'My trouble is – I can't say no and I can't say yes.'

The 'deafies' were foaming at the mouth with excitement on the stairs. When you left the Royal Institute for the Deaf at Gower Street the deaf and staff wept to see you go.

You sold the old house, which you yourself had cleaned from cellar to attic, found a buyer, got the right price, spent two days in bed. Then bought another house not ten miles from the old one, in a rougher area, for exactly the same price. In the first four months it was broken into twice, the back door smashed in with a sledgehammer. Moose began burying his bills in the garden. He drank vodka, came back footless from The Railway Tavern and The Finishing Post His fury was just contained.

Sometimes you said your mother was dying down there at other times you yourself were dying in Finsbury Park. The confusion was total. I didn't know who to believe, nor who was dying.

One night Katie Deering phoned late, saying a friend

wished to speak to me. The name? 'Patricia.' It was you unsober at Athene's. Buzz prayed to the Lord, referring to Him as The Man. The Hereafter would be as bad as this world, run by heavenly Mafia; prayer was a kind of bribe, payola. Katie sat mesmerized before the large colour TV; Torvill and Dean skated *Boléro*; the three kids clung to her, transfixed, thumbs in mouths, Lizzy, Dizzy and Whizzy, watched the skaters twirling.

You yourself had a tendency to bolt. One night after closing-time outside Chicago 20 you abandoned me for the *third* time, fled weeping into the dark. You were feeling edgy, shattered, had gone mad again. If I was a badger, you were a hare, both Pisceans. You wrote me a postcard from Somerset: 'My dear Brian – Going down on the train now. Hawthorn blossom all over the hedges all the way. Snow-in-June. Sally.'

Moose's sister had arrived from Copenhagen. Liza, aged thirteen, worried about her thin ankles and big bust. All the girls in the soccer club were of course Lesbian. Titus, aged eighteen, kept piranha fish, was attacked by vengeful black youths in the school yard. Large coloured youths drove in at recess, to do him properly, because of a quarrel over a coloured girl; he was taken to hospital with fractured ribs and a broken nose. Saxon, your eldest, had been beaten up by his father for giving cheek, answering back.

One Saturday night the stand-off half of Moose's team, having just left The Green Man in an unsober condition, was struck by a white Cortina driven by a Cypriot, and carried as far as the Odeon. He was kept alive in a life-support machine until his parents arrived from Sheffield. He was breathing, but 'had no face to talk with'. They asked that the machine be turned off.

You liked the big city for the edge it gave you, but were 'shattered' once more by events in the country. The deaths of Uncle Gilbert and your grandfather, both in their nineties. You'd remembered the pleasant peaty aroma of old men, when as a child you had sat on their laps, the warmth and protection (more imaginery than real) it afforded.

'Psst, missy! Yuve goota a nice fice, missy!' the tough

coloured youths whispered spookily outside The Court House. A knife was shown, you had to walk the gauntlet of their threats. The attacker was known for previous violent behaviour. You had to give evidence. Then all that trouble ended; the case went to a higher court, the attacker was arrested. He had a record. Titus slept with his bedroom door locked, a shiv under his pillow. Big Mike had done a bunk to Hatfield.

You had not many years to live, you said sadly, showing me your palms. Yet in Glastonbury they lived to a ripe old age – Uncle Gilbert for one. Your moods went on and off like traffic lights. You belonged in spirit to the fast set of a previous time: Emily Coleman and Mary Pyne, the daring lost ones – Thelma Wood accelerating about the Étoile in a red Bugatti with the muffler removed. Stingos at the Dôme. Sipping tea laced with absinthe with McAlmon at the Berlin Adlon.

You, as Harbinger of Woe, went with your dose of bad news every morning to wake up the estranged husband, Moose. Your name, when I did recall it, seemed to suit you, it fitted: Sally Underwood.

You took jobs that were beneath you, worked for a minicab firm, the deaf, kept the family going, knew petty criminals. To the yobbos and geezers you were the witchy-looking bird with the tits. The burglar with revolver in bag had offered you fifty quid to show your breasts. You said you needed the money but not that badly. Moose threw up his job, went bankrupt again, buried his bills in the garden. The VAT man was after him. The Somerset rooks were building high in the trees that spring; but other creatures were on the wing about the rape-fields.

Howling like attacking dervishes, savages at tribal rites deep in the jungle, the damned in deepest Hell, some wildly excited coloured youths were engaging in burying an unconscious drunken comrade in an open drain outside The Green Man on Muswell Hill. 'Darkies', your mother called them. Head-butters were in action between Oscar's and Chicago 20, and Flynn the drug-pusher slinking home.

The Bird I Fancied

*

The small red Bugatti buzzed into Juan-les-Pins with muffler removed, into a broad street with tramlines leading to the harbour, the glittering sea. In the Bar Basque a band was tuning up, before launching into 'I'm Looking For Sally'. The large smiling gent in beige suiting sprawled with legs apart, pulling on a thick cigar, watching us dance over the sanded dance-floor under the turning fairy lights. A sea breeze, smell of resin, cigar smoke, glittering lights.

You, only you; a chestful of breasts, a bird's ever-suspicious eye with permanently enlarged pupils, on the lookout for predators. Slightly knock-kneed, with the inturned toes of a wide-hipped breeder. A warmly sexual nature, the barest hint of a rural burr. Say 'lardy cake'. Say 'Beacon Hill'. Say 'Wells'. Say 'Mendips'. The dark gods of Somerset are listening.

Bugger my old boots, but of all the birds in the air that ever floated on dark water, twittered, hid in reeds, flew in the night, skidded on ice, sang from treetop, perched in impossible places, lamented, rose early, retired late, had young, choked on chicken, reappeared next morning, drank to excess, went on the wagon, regretted nothing, died on the wing, struck against lighthouses, were incapable of restraint, I surely fancied you.

A shadow passing, a female presence gone. As sure as God's in bleeding Gloucestershire, it's true, dear heart.

8
The Dying Hyacinths

One went through a dark hallway and down a step into an old-fashioned low-ceilinged oblong room with wide south windows that gave onto the kitchen proper, leading into a scullery and lean-to where fuel, brushes and cleaning materials were stored. The 'rest' room had an oval table with easy chairs about it, a telephone within easy reach, set on a pile of directories. Here Beamish, Mitzi and Riley spent a deal of time 'unwinding', preparatory to sallying forth to The Alexandra or The Green Man or the off licence for more Diamante. The narrow walled garden was full of ox bones and Riley's generous stools in various stages of reverting back to humus. One could see into the living-room through French windows kept permanently closed. The long living-room had shelves of books, a black leather sofa, piles of magazines, and was rarely used.

Of your parents in Glastonbury you said sadly: 'They see nobody now. Nobody they know. All their real friends are dead. Not much life left in those little grey cells. In the dark wardrobe the hyacinths are not coming up any more.'

I tried to see them dying in Glastonbury, but found it hard to imagine them there.

You were seized with this strange caprice. You wouldn't show up. You just damn well wouldn't. *You'd stand me up.* Overcast days make some people inventive. You didn't play games ('Don't get ideas!'). You were a strange cup of tea.

Love mixed with sexual desire is a game with secret rules. You have to play, learn as you go. Touches are messages in code.

*

A pick-up truck was pulling away from outside Buzz's new place in Coniston Road before I had cognisance of it and could slow up; for the dark shadowy figure who crouched over the wheel, seen through the small mud-splashed rear window, mashing the gears while grimly puffing a fag, might well have been Moose, as I walked slowly towards it, like filings pulled by a magnet. ('Her husband's arriving any minute now to connect up the fridge!' Buzz screeched down the line.)

Curled up in a foetal pose on the rug, smelling powerfully of damp fur and dog, Riley was giving pitiable little whimpers, his hind legs jerking softly in a dream of pursuit and capture.

'Riles is having one of his wet dreams,' Mitzi said fondly, looking down at the whimperer.

'Hunting, more likely,' I said.

'Same thing.'

'I see the Pomeranian ship *Fidelity* sank in the Gulf,' said Beamish, turning over a page of *The Times* with a purposeful rustle.

'Fancy that,' Mitzi said, doing her gollywog act.

Moose was rocketing down the M1 out of London in his pick-up truck, exceeding the speed limit, duffing up heavies in strange pubs, having his front teeth knocked out at rough rugger, cooking for the three who were missing you, marvelling at you in the bath, implanting a warm kiss on your warm groin. 'It's a long way from Uruguay to Berlin,' murmured Moose, lingering on the *beso*.

Usually he said nothing, just glared. Many jealous ones are silent. That is to say, those ravaged by jealousy can conceal it, by saying nothing.

'Mighty pretty country around 'ere,' murmured Moose, laying his hand on meat.

You removed his hand.

'Heaven's breath,' muttered the flustered Moose, 'Heaven's breath smells wooingly 'ere.'

You were silent, just breathing, aloof from rut.

'The breezy call of incense-breathing morn,' Moose said with a heavy sigh.

Silence, your freezing aloofness.

'The Chambers made of Amber that is clear,' murmured the Moose gone all poetic, 'doth give a fine sweet smell if fire be near.'

Prolonged silence. (You have left the room.)

'Have a gander at this.'

'Arse over tea-kettle.'

'A small little black left-handed batsman?'

'I was sitting inside in The Pig.'

'Squeamish?'

'He can also use the bat, can Richard 'Adlee.'

The voices in The Prince droned on. Soon it would be closing time in the afternoon. Through the deforming coloured rhomboids of the window I caught sight of the actor Michael Gough passing by, looking haggard.

'Oi 'ad visions of gettin' m'gear together,' a resigned voice said down the bar.

'A load of codswallop.'

Contracting and expanding, turning orange and opaque, the sad figure passed out of sight.

You phoned me under a number of patently false names ('Patricia' of the BBC, 'Mary-Lou' of the Caledonian); none of these disguises deceived Margaret, who passed on the message sourly: 'Your flibbertigibbet wishes to speak to you.' Or, more sourly: 'The whore phoned yesterday.'

Tout va changer. Margaret knew how to unsettle me, suffering her rancour. A secret worm eats into a pear.

'He said I'd be more comfortable waiting upstairs, but we were hardly in the door when the trousers were off.'

False Stavros of Athene's.

The coarse Liverpudlian Freddy was winking and nodding by the service-hatch.

'I could never give up beer because I'd be terribly constipated,' said the boozy voice. 'I feel bad now, but I'd feel much worse if I didn't drink.'

'Living most chastely in Colchester.'
'Well pissed was the vendor of shoes.'
'Pansies are thirsty little buggers!'
'The bloody cats must go.'
'I had a wet dream.'

Nettles love to grow near ruins, the contemplation of which (the ruins) is said to be a masculine speciality. But why?

Your courtship sounded most odd. As far as I could gather Moose took you straight to bed, after which he marched you into the nearest jeweller's and bought a ring, made you pregnant with Saxon; and hardly had you expelled your second, Titus, than little Liza was on the way. Before one could say coil or condom you were already the mother of three, and Moose had already begun burying his bills in the garden.

One afternoon on the balcony, looking down into the Patch, the cemented compound where the kids played, where the two sycamores had been cut down by Haringey Council, I saw a little girl walking alone there, shouting 'Fuck! . . . Fuck!'

Along a wall by Hyde Park tube someone had painted in white capital letters this high-flown sentiment: 'THERE IS NO HEAT GREATER THAN LUST, NO ILLUSION GREATER THAN LIES'.

Moose had been a dancer, as his mother had been in Capetown; but had put on too much weight and had to give it up. He went into the building (or was it demolition?) trade instead. He was not a man one would care to encounter when his dander was up; and by all accounts it was up most of the time. I was having a quiet drink by myself in The Rose and Crown one day and Freddy Byswater and his mate the architect were playing a game of darts, Freddy throwing the arrows' in an ill-tempered way, effing and blinding, bad-mouthing minority sects, cursing the Jewish orphan girl behind the bar in The Prince. He drank with Moose in The Railway Tavern and The Finishing Post, and now he came to stand beside me. He also fancied you. I asked him: 'What kind of chap is this Moose?' 'Moose Underwood?' said Freddy, giving me a leery look. 'Over six foot of meanness – I wouldn't care to cross old Moose.'

Your friend Fedelma had 'hardly eaten in six weeks', lovely as Audrey Hepburn.

'I don't think Audrey Hepburn is any way lovely,' I said. 'Is your friend anorexic?'

'She has cancer.'

On the Barnet bus a mad Negro was shouting out curses and maledictions, threatening the end of the world, but no Barnet skinheads were aboard, setting out for a night of wog-bashing aggro.

You and Moose slept apart, in different rooms on different floors, or you slept with Liza, who was in trouble with the black kids at school for being the sister of Titus who had been beaten up by a black gang for going out with one of their sisters.

'Pussy,' they whispered creepily. 'You've got a nice pussy, missy!'

'My nipples are sore,' you said.

In a park where coloured people strolled about near Highbury Corner I saw a man with a civet on a lead. The civet came sniffing and crawled over my foot; I felt that strange quick furtive life down there. Two coloured girls stopped to admire the civet. The owner of the civet spoke to them in their own language.

'Come and get me,' the loved voice said on the line. 'Can I pop around for half an hour?' was another ploy. Sometimes I was working on something, sometimes it was late at night ('Come out for a walk'), once I was asked to join you around midnight in a French friend's house in Hampstead. Once you attempted to force an entrance past Margaret at the door.

Cloudy days make some people inventive. When a thing is shapen, wrote Chaucer, it shall be. You belonged to the misty lost world of Claude Autant-Lara and *Le Diable au Corps*, of fleshly pleasure and retribution and of joy. You

202

were not very good, as you put it, at correcting your instincts. Glastonbury seemed to me a magical place. In the abbey there were buried St Patrick, St Benedict Biscop, Blessed Aidan and the Venerable Bede himself, immured with Henry of Blois and Adam of Sodbury. Joseph had come bearing two cruets of the holy blood and sweat.

You too came from the country.

In the end you told me that it was Murky Murchison ('someone you know'), at the heel of the hunt, who had had you twice or more in your bedroom where I had never been and in a hotel in Glastonbury into which the be-blazered brandy-voiced cad had inveigled you (had it been all that difficult?). When he had copulated with you, no doubt whispering brandy endearments into your ear, you wept. The heart tormented and buried; unbroken pain receding under this grey sky? I tried to imagine it, but could not. I tried to 'forgive' your misdemeanour, if that be the correct term.

> *Fancy passed me by*
> *And nothing will remain . . .*

'Nobaddy but yew!' bawled the male 'vocalist' hidden in the innards of the *Schlagermusik*machine with its red, green and orange lights pulsing fiercely in the lounge of The Nightingale, to my acute discomfort, prolonging the agony of *yeee-oooOOOOW*. You ordered a round for us at the bar, spoke to a total stranger.

It's Saturday again and there's a rush on curtains at Underwoods.

'The bloody lifts are all up the creek,' said an irate male voice down the bar. Trapped in the box mechanically flashing lights the vocalist went on howling.

'Prudence,' I counselled you, 'prudence in all things.'

You gave me your horse-eyed look through your mane, put down the White Shield and the Ramrod.

'No, 'e don't do no work . . . 'e don't do nuffin'.'

'Eeee, looverly stoof!'

9
Fallen Leaves

'The leaves are turning,' you said on Barnet Common. All the wood was bronze and golden and 'it was ending'. You tried to catch a small jumping frog in your cupped hand but instead caught a grasshopper. I found a dappled glade under an old beech tree where previous lovers had cut their initials and entwined hearts and another hand had cut FUCK and CUNT the much-abused synecdoche. Scabby and sore-looking the cuts were closing up, the resin set hard as amber. I had you twice in Hadley Wood and afterwards we dozed near a path in a meadow. It was the first time in six months. You told me that Moose was suffering from pains in his left ball, and that a jadeite axe from Scandinavia, six thousand years old, from the Later Bronze Age, had been dug up in a 'sweat-trench' near Glastonbury. We slept in the warm meadow, out of sight, and at opening time went into the cool of Ye Olde Moncken Holt in Barnet village to drink foaming pints of Directors' ale.

You told me that your friend had died of cancer, you were 'disconsolate', you were thinking of going to Italy for a short holiday. You had another friend there with a place near the border.

'Which border?'
'The French.'
'Can I come?'
'Don't be silly.'

I did not want you to go. We had more Directors'. Alternatively you thought of Somerset. There was a beach, driftwood, a cottage.

When with you I seemed far removed from you. Not

seeing you for months at a time I felt closer to you. You reproached me for my many shortcomings. I was 'not to be trusted'; I 'threatened' you; you remembered 'all the bad times'; you 'feared me'.

'You wouldn't put yourself on the line for me.'

'What we need is a dappled glade,' you said. Hadley Wood was sparse in undergrowth but was infested with clumps of briar mixed with tangles of fern and nettles. The sun did not penetrate into any of the grassy places and I seemed to walk in circles with you following as if reluctantly until we broke through a stand of beech saplings and over a horse ride and there before us was an old beech tree and under it grass and sun, where you at once took off your shoes, began undressing, with sun pouring through the foliage above onto the dead leaves on the grassy place, the veritable 'dappled glade', where I had you twice, after a long half year of abstinence. We were back in the land of the harmattan. I saw the projecting rim of the Djenne mosque with its multiplication of phallic parts standing out like up-ended shell-cases as part of the roof, protecting us from the fierce sun in the country of the Dogon and Folani, given to inbreeding, pestered by tsetse-flies. We were again Walkers in the Dream, going naked, hand in hand through the cool granaries dug out of the Bandiagara cliffs, a natural fortress, and isolated there for six hundred years or more, and a third time I enjoyed you on a hill of wheat. And you so beautiful below me with closed eyes and drenched armpits said my name over and over between clenched teeth: 'Bludgeon, Bludgeon, you *Dagana* . . .' and I came alive again. I could feel the fierce sun cracking the roof high above us, but the cave was cool, a whole series of great cool interleading caves with mountains of grain piled up and up in cavern after cavern going back into the deep recesses of the mountain.

As the change from childish innocence to traumatic adulthood had been rapid (overnight?), so the change from girlhood to womanhood (the rape in Glastonbury?); you still carried the taint with you and no boyfriend could cure you. Your dark good looks were a curse. You were addicted to *amour fou*, of deliberately inflicting pain on the lover who never would be able to forget you. You had a sultry Italian look, strong feeling agitating your bosom. You were not a country nor a city girl but rather a party from some bygone time – Maria Casares hanging up washing on a line in *Les Enfants du Paradis* (a coded French film about the Nazi occupation), or Mary of Modena the consort of James II, twenty-five years his junior ('eyes which had wept but were black and beautiful'). You were *infected* with the past.

Madame Lauriol de Barney!

(Lilli Palmer?)

You were friendly with Nick the Murderer, Bill the Burglar, Mickey the Jeweller and Jeff's father Les, a villain's runner of the old school, minder of a gang pub in Brick Lane when crime was an honest profession, or so we were led to believe. They all knew you, liked you in The Prince, no doubt thinking: *Stacked!*

When we left I read on a dead-end wall:

CANE MY BUM,
SUCK MY TITS,
FUCK MY CUNT

where the road tilted down to show London and its tower blocks shrouded in a blue haze. And another cramped hand had written:

IMMANUEL KANT RULES!

Moose again resigned from his job, began burying bills in the garden. Ten years of misunderstanding had elapsed in your marriage, and shared between you 'an inability to say what's wrong'. You spoke up but he wouldn't listen to you.

'Why separate?' Moose asked.

You went again to Glastonbury, where your mother was no better. She had taken up embroidery.

'Is there another? . . . I don't mean to pry.'

Not half.

'Leave 'im, the blightah,' Old Nutt advised.

You returned to London.

'It's not working out,' Saxon said.
'I know.'

You don't see me,' you said. 'You don't look at me.' A wild
dark-veiled ('the afterglow of spent beauty'?), distraught
look. The dark hair combed down over the eyes: the Mata
Hari look. You handed me a snapshot of Moose dripping wet
in a shower-stall, a strapping handsome fellow with the big
semi-erection of Prehistoric Man.
'Who took the photo?'
You told me stories of Somerset, of the Mendip Hills, of the
blue pools between the mining dumps, of the river flooding
in winter, calm cats licking their fur on windowsills or
stretched out on the lower branches of apple trees; it
sounded like the Garden of Eden.
Ah Mendips! haunt of adders.
'I cannot keep track of my disappointments.'
Dreaming of me, of us together, you had shouted out in
your sleep 'Suck me! Suck me!' and woken Moose, driving
him crazy again. He was taking you four or five times a night,
like Boswell with Louisa the actress; and you couldn't do
anything, because it would only have made it worse.
From Moose's fiery gorge, like smoke, rushed upwards all
the words he spoke . . .
Two photos were hidden under your clothes in a chest of
drawers in your room where I had never been. One showed
an unshaven fellow photographed in snow at Parc St-Maur
in the outskirts of Paris; the other showed you brown as a
sultana after your holiday at Lyme Regis. They were 'lying
face to face' in the bottom drawer. You and I: Brian and
sultry Sally.
In the meantime we were meeting and mating surrepti-
tiously as hares, those furtive and ungainly creatures so
attached to out-of-the-way places, who run in circles, box
on their hind legs, go mad in March, scream while being torn
to bits by greyhounds. Our totem animal by rights should
not have been the Fish but the Hare that lives precariously
by flight and escape. We were camouflaged in rather similar
two-tone outfits. Your tufted armpits my idea, for I liked

your sweat; again a cause of suspicion with Moose, who preferred you shaven. We were secretive as hares, as fungal agents, the pair of us.

Was I attracted to you, as you sometimes liked to suggest, because you reminded me of somebody else, or did I want you because you belonged to somebody else? One night in bed in the West Wing I called you by another name. Your scream and the blow to the face were simultaneous. I caught hold of you, pinned your arms, otherwise you might have jumped out of your skin. Leaping out of bed you were struggling into your clothes, phoning a minicab, cursing me. I heard the murmurings of Beamish and his lady in the bedroom next to ours. It was bang in the middle of the Muswell Hill night.

'You don't see me,' your repeated accusation. 'You wouldn't search for me unless you'd already found me. If you don't remember me, then I can't exist.

'I'll come looking for you when you least desire me.'

'And when would that be?' I asked.

The dregs of the city's sad love comes to us in the whirlwind (*la hojarasca*). A face full of shocking desires. *En el reino del amor huesped extrano* – a strange guest in the kingdom of love. *Polvo enamorado.*

'You had me in Havendon Wood.'

'I had you twice in Havendon Wood.'

Then you went away again. And I was alone, standing by Biggles in The Prince of Wales one grey evening, Biggles with his tot of Teacher's casting a speculative brown eye at cirro-cumulus massing over Pond Square and drifting on over Hampstead Heath, excellent cover for Sopwith Camels to hide in and emerge suddenly with machine-guns stuttering at intruding Fokkers, Huns.

'Gimme a pils,' said a soft-voiced man.

'Cooney hit the canvas twice,' boomed another man down the bar.

'A touch of autumn out there I fancy,' Biggles said quietly to me.

10
Adieu, Annie Laurie!

he schooner docks alongside the little pier. On the sea a painted
ip made of cardboard. The girl immediately prepares to leave for
era Cruz. What rotten luck! The night is rife with peril.

ou were devious, untrustworthy, bitchy and intractable,
ifficult (sometimes impossible) to get on with, wrapped in
dness and a compulsive liar, the one who can't or won't
ll the truth. In other words, a true female.

I knew you as trustworthy and honest and believed you as
uch as I believed anybody. You were a lost thing, as the
ish sea eagle (extinct since 1898), the striped bass of the
udson River, the flaming maple forests of Vermont.

You told Mitzi: 'We can't be friends. Because you make all
y confidences public.' Sadly Mitzi agreed. She and
eamish were incurable gossips, never off the telephone,
ver tired of rehashing stories. They were both twittery,
eir spurious gaiety a form of hysteria, and much given to
rsiflage.

Adieu, adieu, my Sally, you will ever be my Annie Laurie
d I'll never forget you, dear Hard-to-Find. *Warte nur; bald*
hest du auch. Wait awhile; soon you too will rest.

Beneath the Ice-shelf

1974

One hundred and sixty years ago in the dreadful frost and snow at the beginning of 1814, kind-hearted Charles Lamb was out in all weathers, visiting the imprisoned Leigh Hunt who had been put away for two years for ridiculing the Prince Regent. Hyde Park was then littered with dirty people and provisions (not that much has changed in the interval), Mary Lamb had toothache very badly and was about to go mad again. Insanity ran in the Lamb family like a streak through Brighton rock.

Trust I find you in fine fettle, friend. Stay well muffled up. Up here in the Pennines they still count sheep in the old lingo. *Bumfit*. Deep snow still lingering on here where none in their right minds would go marching. Down below in murky Birmingham it's all Bingobongobanga I can tell you. The soccer Yahoos prowl about with skulls shaven to the pluck in the manner of convicts in Dickens's day, invoking Magwitch and the hulks. Their looks of fixed hostility bode ill for old England. The pro football season gets into its swing with a ritual killing. But this generally happens away from the actual arena where 'supporters' or rival gangs of thugs are constrained behind moats and high wire fences, as in the days of chivalry when maidens were locked away in towers. The hot whiffling puppies run amok after the game, and the great mindless commonalty go in outright fear of them. But you know a nation is finished anyway when it produces postage stamps such as this with image of your dyspeptic sovereign affixed to this *carta*.

However, spring must pull us round again. This muck cannot endure forever. Didn't I hear the children scream

213

'Yellow!' almost a month ago? Feathered songsters will soon be on the job. Weather will be dull but extraordinarily mild, with grass sprouting out of season, honeysuckle bursting prodigiously, awaiting another nip of frost to kill it. Geese honking whilst assaulting the wet uplands with soft grey shit, appropriate emblem for a whoreson year not unfree of general adversity, no by God. Keep thy head well covered.

I rarely venture down below except for absolute necessities such as Scotch and tobacco, carbon paper. From my bedroom I survey the rolling fells, a name I've always liked, the fells, where today a gruesomely active crow, very black against the virgin snow, feeds on the eyes of a dead sheep, only the stricken head emerging ghost-like from the drifts. The immediate ambience is now mercifully rid of the sound of polite handclapping followed by communal gusts of infectious laughter, for I have persuaded the obliging landlady to remove the offending Box. The times are even worse than those envisaged by Orwell who admittedly was ill; and we still have some way to go.

'I *still* value human life, in spite of everything,' I overhead a sagacious Parsnip say in a frightfully Punjabi-wallah-y voice from a lounge bar I just happened to stumble into a week or so ago. What kind of life had this wag in mind, do you suppose? The Gulf Oil man in natty blue company overalls spoke knowingly of pressures and borings to a hotel commissionaire who displayed all that starched and bluff rigidity that told of previous army training.

Mad scientists, said the Gulf Oil man, drilling through a lost undersea world beneath the Ross ice-shelf in Antarctica, had come upon life-forms and fossils dating back fourteen million years, and were attempting to discover what kind of creatures could have evolved in waters which had not seen sunlight for more than ten thousand years, with water temperature hovering just above freezing. Wilkinson's blades for a close easy shave.

Meanwhile the long injurious winter is showing no sign of ending, releasing its iron grip. I live just on the snowline, now general, in a peeling late Victorian mansion that might still appeal to Charles Addams, wrapped up in blankets before a coal fire in a house wanting repairs in all essentials, staring into the birch tree in the garden, in it some birds which I attempt to identify through opera-glasses bought twenty years ago in Canal Street for one dollar, when life was still possible there. Doors hang on their hinges by the skin of their teeth and the lot is mortgaged to the hilt. I snowshoe over the white fells to a rude bar patronized by those hardy souls who walk the Pennine Way, ending up in a far-off Escotia amid the hoarfrost. Below in the haunt of skinheads and punks, thick and squat or leery and lank, truculence and insolence inextricably mixed, you have coal-smog in the plundered glass-walled valley where the heart shrinks as the stench freezes the mind, converts it into authentic minerals. Some lost soul plays grim Baptist hymns on an old diseased church organ in a deserted church in Coke-on-Ende into which I happened to stagger, looking for grace but found only dark choirstalls, mildewed prayer books, a booming organ, the odours of bygone piety and lost congregations, the wind moaning through the leaded windows, and a redheaded lunatic in a chalky black smock pedalling away for dear life, head down as if passing into a headwind, drawing almighty wheezes from the antiquated pipes. I crept out, ashamed of what I had seen, as far as I can now recall.

The Venerable Bede of Jarrow did not hold overmuch with birthdays and suchlike frippery; what mattered more to him was the day of a man's death and the passage into everlasting life. So, *Glückwünsche und Mähs* (goat), as I believe yours falls about now and raise a brimming beaker in your direction. All the very best, friend. Stay well. Gather thyself unto the old things.

We live in squeamish times.

Anthony Burgess at the London Savoy

1980

In the dimly expiring late October afternoon light a family of inbeciles huddle by a traffic jam, viewing a poster for the *Ken Dodd Laughter Show*. Idiot smiles fixed and upstanding hair stiff as yardbrushes, they cry *'Tatty-by! Tatty-by!'* in high freak voices.

My taxi-man can speak four languages. Rain begins to fall as your correspondent enters the rich precincts of the Savoy Hotel, where famed soft-porn authoress Erica Jong has *not* booked in, following a murder on the top floor. Air-conditioning keeps the flowers fresh in the vestibule where floorwalkers and house detectives in dark suiting move sombre as undertaker's mutes. A great coal fire burns in the grate. The PA machine is tirelessly extruding news of world-wide calamities and the latest war news: ISRAELI JETS ATTACK *tackatatackata* LEBANON COAST *tickeytoc* DUPONT'S £4 MILLION LOSSES *ticketyboom*. Mr Burgess, whom I have already met at the Hutchinson launch, arrives with entourage exactly seven minutes late. Effusive apologies.

We ascend slowly to a high suite overlooking the Thames and a vision of never-ceasing traffic headlights moving through the murk. A broad bridge seen through an open window. A leg-brace supports itself against one wall. Mr Burgess orders strong coffee, offers Scotch; the entourage retires to another room.

Anticipating a blustery manner and possible truculence, judge of our surprise to encounter a tall handsome man in liturgical shirt set off by red tie, hair a sable silver, manicured nails, no discernible accent, the slitty eyes of a fellow inured to a hot climate (Malta, Malaya, Borneo); a *reserved*

219

affability. Most happy to be interviewed for the new *Sunday Tribune*.

The dollar millionaire has just published his twenty-sixth work of fiction, *Earthly Powers*, for which Messrs Hutchinson stumped up a rumoured £75,000 advance. Already 9,000 copies have been subscribed from an initial print-run of 15,000. Michael Korda, editor-in-chief of Simon and Schuster, paid a rumoured $400,000 (say £170,000).

The Booker Prize went to the sage of Bowerchalke, who came up to Stationers' Hall from rural Wilts. Agent Deborah Rogers is said to have sold movie rights of *Clockwork Orange* for a paltry £400 four years back; but there again the English rights of *Waiting for Godot* went for half that.

Mr Burgess himself was not too happy with Kubrick's explicitly horrorful angle, and was alarmed by the resultant murders, following screenings. CHAOS ODER ANARCHIE, the wall graffiti proclaimed. LEV LESBISK. GLOO IS LUVE. Gobbledegook was on the rise, the eye radiantly preparing for death.

Mr Burgess, unsolicited, recalls early days of poverty, as if it had not been his very own bread and dripping. School-master Devar brought two copies of *Ulysses* into Manchester, secreted upon his person in order to pass undetected through the customs, the same customs that burnt 2,000 copies in 1922.

In 1959 he was given a year to live; overwork had taken its toll, a suspected tumour of the brain. He had churned out five novels at the rate of 2,000 words a day in one year. 'Fecundity is not a good sign?' The eyes narrow behind a cloud of Daneman cigar-smoke. 'You've got to write – keep at it.'

He was teaching in Borneo then, couldn't find a job in England, pensioned off. 'A thousand pounds was a lot in 1957.' He believes in the Word. In 1965 his first wife died. He soon remarried, to the Italian contessa; they make their own deals, rumoured to be stiff. His work – some fifty titles now – goes into translations. Publishers may speak of a continuing slump, but Mr Burgess goes on churning it out, novels, oratorios, reviews and articles, screenplays.

He had thought to take a sabbatical in Dublin, show his Italian wife 'another kind of Catholicism'; nothing came of that. He accepted no state grants, Arts Council handouts; all revenue came via his strong right hand. He was with Jack McGowran the day before he died, of a heart-attack in the Algonquin. A fund for the Irish actor was started, funds collected, but it was 'too late anyway'.

He would like to write a play about John Calvin; tried to set up a film based on John Hawkes's *The Lime Twig*. Composed music for the bassoon, spoke with Borges in Middle English to baffle the Perón spies. He is sixty-three but doesn't look it, fears his memory is going, but it isn't. His son Andreas wears a kilt, wants to be a Scotsman, doesn't wish to write.

Cranks phone in the middle of the night – another *Clockwork Orange*-type murder – your comment? 'People like war. It's like art, has a beginning and an end.' The ghosted book with Ingrid Bergman was just a rumour; Anthony Burgess is no ghost. I complain that there are no meals in *Earthly Powers*, a real book of fiction must have a meal in it. He reaches out, finds a page, shows me a meal; well, a list of stuff to eat. It seems ungracious to dislike the novel; but the author does not much concern himself with this. It was a year's work, discarded before, taken up again, finished; there are other books to be written. I pick a page at random: 'Hellsmoke curled from the gratings. Red and yellow light flashed on and off faces of gratuitous malevolence.'

He admires the gentle Svevo, Corvo's *Hadrian the Seventh*, Faulkner's 'harmonics', Joyce for his everything. The T. S. Eliot Memorial Lecture at Kent was delivered extempore, *con brio*, broadcast. I heard it; the audience was dominated and could only titter. He set out to prove connections between linguistics on the page and tonal structures in music, compared 'The Wreck of the Deutschland' and *Finnegans Wake*. A witty defence of obscurity.

He can be witty, but the fun comes rather grimly. The host is standing now, fingers clamped rigid like Beckett's on the cigar (Beckett's brand too), the noble head enveloped in Daneman smoke. A kind man withal, considerate of others, with few bad words to say of his fellow scribes. He fell foul of Professor Ricks and Saul Bellow, for reasons unclear. Mr Burgess shows me politely to the door of his high suite, offers a firm handclasp, specific advice. 'Work! . . . Work!' his last words on the slowly closing door, the narrowed Burgess eyes. The entourage are silent still in another room, holding their collective breath.

In the murky Strand a peevish voice cries out: 'You flash cunt you, I 'ope yow wreck yow fukken caw!'

I wish Mr Burgess well in the rough times ahead. Our times.